California

Everyday
Mathematics®

The University of Chicago School Mathematics Project

Student Math Journal
Volume 2

Grade

 Wright Group

The McGraw·Hill Companies

The University of Chicago School Mathematics Project (UCSMP)

Max Bell, Director, UCSMP Elementary Materials Component; Director, *Everyday Mathematics* First Edition
James McBride, Director, *Everyday Mathematics* Second Edition
Andy Isaacs, Director, *Everyday Mathematics* Third Edition
Amy Dillard, Associate Director, *Everyday Mathematics* Third Edition

Authors

Max Bell	Andy Isaacs	Amy Dillard	Kathleen Pitvorec
Jean Bell	James McBride	Robert Hartfield	Peter Saecker
John Bretzlauf	Cheryl G. Moran*		

Third Edition only

Technical Art
Diana Barrie

Teachers in Residence
Kathleen Clark, Patti Satz

Editorial Assistant
John Wray

Contributors

Robert Balfanz, Judith Busse, Mary Ellen Dairyko, Lynn Evans, James Flanders, Dorothy Freedman,
Nancy Guile Goodsell, Pam Guastafeste, Nancy Hanvey, Murray Hozinsky, Deborah Arron Leslie,
Sue Lindsley, Mariana Mardrus, Carol Montag, Elizabeth Moore, Kate Morrison, William D. Pattison,
Joan Pederson, Brenda Penix, June Ploen, Herb Price, Dannette Riehle, Ellen Ryan, Marie Schilling,
Susan Sherrill, Patricia Smith, Robert Strang, Jaronda Strong, Kevin Sweeney, Sally Vongsathorn,
Esther Weiss, Francine Williams, Michael Wilson, Izaak Wirzup

Photo Credits

©Fotosearch, p. v *bottom*; Getty Images, cover, *right*; ©Linda Lewis; Frank Lane Picture Agency/CORBIS, cover, *bottom left*; ©Photodisc/Getty Images, p. v *top*; ©Star/zefa/Corbis, cover, *center*.

California *Everyday Mathematics* Reviewers

Dr. Dale Oliver, Humboldt State University
Dr. Bill Jacobs, University of California, Santa Barbara

Dr. Elizabeth Burroughs, Humboldt State University
Dr. Alfred Manaster, University of California, San Diego

www.WrightGroup.com

 **Wright Group**

Send all inquiries to:
Wright Group/McGraw-Hill
P.O. Box 812960
Chicago, IL 60681

ISBN 978-0-07-609798-2
MHID 0-07-609798-6

10 QDB 13 12

The *McGraw·Hill* Companies

Contents

UNIT 8 Fractions

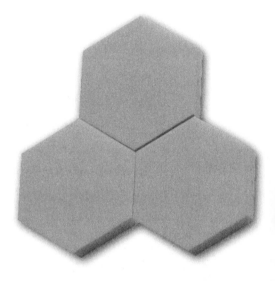

UNIT 9 Measurement

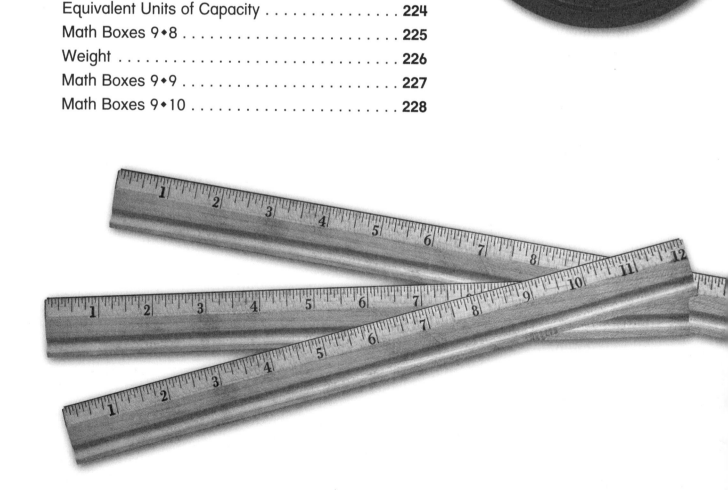

UNIT 10 Decimals and Place Value

UNIT 11 Whole Number Operations Revisited

$0.84

$3.41

UNIT 12 Year-End Reviews and Extensions

Activity Sheets

**LESSON
7·1**   **Using a Calculator to Find Patterns**

1. Use a calculator to count by 5s starting with the number 102.
Color the counts on the grid with a crayon. Look for a pattern.

									100
101	102	103	104	105	106	107	108	109	110
111	112	113	114	115	116	117	118	119	120
121	122	123	124	125	126	127	128	129	130

2. Pick a number to count by. Start with a number less than 310.
Use your calculator to count. Record your counts on the grid with
a crayon.

									300
301	302	303	304	305	306	307	308	309	310
311	312	313	314	315	316	317	318	319	320
321	322	323	324	325	326	327	328	329	330
331	332	333	334	335	336	337	338	339	340
341	342	343	344	345	346	347	348	349	350
351	352	353	354	355	356	357	358	359	360
361	362	363	364	365	366	367	368	369	370

I counted by _____ starting with the number _____.

Here is a pattern that I found: _____

_____

LESSON 7·1 Math Boxes

---

1. Which one is certain to happen? Circle the best answer.

A. A spaceship will land at school.

B. Your favorite sports team will win every time.

C. Spring will follow winter.

D. You will be a movie star.

2. Solve.

Unit ____

$17 - 9 =$ _____

$27 - 9 =$ _____

$57 - 9 =$ _____

_____ $= 77 - 9$

_____ $= 97 - 9$

3. Make a 7-by-7 array with dots.

How many in all? _____ dots

4. Arrange the allowances in order from the minimum (smallest) to the maximum (largest).

$10, $3, $7, $1, $4

_____, _____, _____, _____, _____

The minimum is _____.

The maximum is _____.

MRB 45

5. Match each person with the correct weight.

newborn   about 144 pounds

2nd grader   about 63 pounds

adult   about 7 pounds

6. How many boxes are on this Math Boxes page?

_____ boxes

How many boxes are on $\frac{1}{2}$ of this page?

_____ boxes

---

1) MR 2.0   2) AF 1.3   3) NS 3.1
4) SDAP 1.3 5) NS 6.1   6) NS 4.2

LESSON 7·2 Making 10s

Record three rounds of *Hit the Target.*

Example Round:

Target number: __40__

Starting Number	Change	Result	Change	Result	Change	Result
12	+38	50	−10	40		

Round 1

Target number: _____

Starting Number	Change	Result	Change	Result	Change	Result

Round 2

Target number: _____

Starting Number	Change	Result	Change	Result	Change	Result

Round 3

Target number: _____

Starting Number	Change	Result	Change	Result	Change	Result

LESSON 7·2 Solving Subtraction Problems

Use base-10 blocks to help you subtract.

1.
longs	cubes
5	6
− 3	9

2.
longs	cubes
7	3
− 1	4

Use any strategy to solve.

3. Ballpark estimate:

_____

47
−19

4. Ballpark estimate:

_____

88
− 23

5. Ballpark estimate:

_____

82
− 65

6. Ballpark estimate:

_____

64
− 38

Number Sense 2.0; Number Sense 2.2

Date _____ Time _____

1. 24 children. 6 in each row.
   Draw an array.

   How many rows?_____ rows

   How many children left over?

   _____ children

2. 15 dogs.
   13 cats.
   12 birds.

   How many animals?

   _____ animals

3. Fill in the missing numbers.

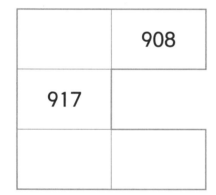

908

917

4. Draw a line of symmetry on this triangle.

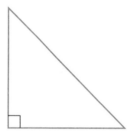

5. Find the rule. Complete the table.

in	out
193	183
232	222
441	
	346

6. _____ of the shape is shaded. Circle the best answer.

   A. $\frac{2}{2}$

   B. $\frac{1}{2}$

   C. $\frac{1}{4}$

   D. 0

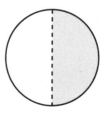

LESSON 7·3 Playing *Basketball Addition*

Materials	☐ *Basketball Addition* scoreboard (*Math Journal 2*, p. 167 or *Math Masters*, p. 451)
	☐ 3 regular dice
Players	2 teams of 3–5 players each
Skill	Add three or more 1- and 2-digit numbers
Object of the Game	To score a greater number of points

Directions

1. Players on opposite teams take turns rolling the 3 dice.

2. Each player enters the sum of the numbers on the 3 dice in the Points Scored table.

3. After each player on a team has rolled the dice, each team finds the total number of points scored by their team for the first half of the game and enters the Team Score in the table.

4. Players repeat Steps 1–3 to find their team's score for the second half of the game.

5. Each team adds their team totals from both halves of the game to find their team's final score.

6. The team with the greater number of points wins the game.

Number Sense 2.0, 2.3; Algebra and Functions **1.1**

LESSON 7·3 *Basketball Addition*

Points Scored	Team 1		Team 2	
	1st Half	**2nd Half**	**1st Half**	**2nd Half**
Player 1				
Player 2				
Player 3				
Player 4				
Player 5				
Team Score				

Point Totals	1st Half	2nd Half	Final
Team 1	_____	_____	_____
Team 2	_____	_____	_____

1. Which team won the first half? _____

   By how much? _____ points

2. Which team won the second half? _____

   By how much? _____ points

3. Which team won the game? _____

   By how much? _____ points

LESSON 7·3 More Multiplication Number Stories

Write your own multiplication stories and draw pictures of your stories. You can use the pictures at the side of the page for ideas.

For each story:

◆ Write the words.

◆ Draw a picture.

◆ Write the answer.

Example:

There are 5 tricycles. How many wheels in all?

Answer: ___*15 wheels*___
　　　　　(unit)

A person has 2 ears.

A tricycle has 3 wheels.

A car has 4 wheels.

The box has 12 crayons.

1. _____

　_____

Answer: _____
　　　　　　(unit)

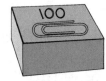

The box has
100 paper clips.

2. _____

　_____

Answer: _____
　　　　　　(unit)

The juice pack
has 6 cans.

Number Sense **3.0**; Mathematical Reasoning 1.0

Math Boxes

1. Which one is impossible? Choose the best answer.

⚬ I will write a letter to a friend.

⚬ I will eat a piece of cake.

⚬ The sun will shine.

⚬ A fish will live out of water.

2. Solve.

Unit

_____ = 37 + 9

_____ = 137 + 9

116 − 8 = _____

176 − 8 = _____

3. Draw 5 fish bowls and 2 fish in each bowl.

How many fish in all?

_____ fish

4. Arrange the number of pets in order from the minimum (smallest) to the maximum (largest).

7, 0, 4, 1, 3, 5, 2

—, —, —, —, —, —, —

The maximum is _____.

The minimum is _____.

5. 1 bag of sugar weighs 5 pounds.

6 bags of sugar weigh

_____ pounds.

A. 50   **B.** 60

C. 25   **D.** 30

6. Circle the trapezoid that has $\frac{1}{3}$ shaded.

LESSON 7·4   The Wubbles

1. On each line, write the number of Wubbles after doubling.
   Use your calculator to help you.

   You started on Friday with _____ Wubble.

   On Saturday, there were _____ Wubbles.

   On Sunday, there were _____ Wubbles.

   On Monday, there will be _____ Wubbles.

   On Tuesday, there will be _____ Wubbles.

   On Wednesday, there will be _____ Wubbles.

   On Thursday, there will be _____ Wubbles.

   On Friday, there will be _____ Wubbles.

A Wubble

2. On each line, write the number of Wubbles
   after halving. Use your calculator to help you.
   Remember that " $\frac{1}{2}$ of " means "divide by 2."

   There were _____ Wubbles.

   After Wink 1, there were _____ Wubbles.

   After Wink 2, there were _____ Wubbles.

   After Wink 3, there were _____ Wubbles.

   After Wink 4, there were _____ Wubbles.

   After Wink 5, there were _____ Wubbles.

   After Wink 6, there were _____ Wubbles.

   After Wink 7, there was _____ Wubble.

Your room could look like
this! What will you do?

Adapted with permission from *Calculator Mathematics Book
2* by Sheila Sconiers, pp. 10 and 11 (Everyday Learning
Corporation, © 1990 by the University of Chicago).

NS **3.1**, 4.0; SDAP **2.0**, 2.1; MR 3.0

LESSON 7·4   Math Boxes

---

1. Collect 29 counters.
How many groups of 3
can you make?

_____ groups

How many counters are
left over?

_____ counters

MRB
114 115

---

2. Solve.

$4 + 3 + 13 =$ _____

_____ $= 12 + 6 + 8$

$5 + 4 + 18 =$ _____

_____ $= 18 + 12 + 6$

$40 = 15 + 6 +$ _____

Unit
train
cars

---

3. Fill in the missing numbers.

717

---

4. Draw the lines of symmetry on
this rectangle.

How many lines of symmetry

are there? _____

MRB
60

5.

Rule	in	out
Double	2	4
	4	
	5	
		14

---

6. Shade one half of this square.

LESSON 7·5   **Math Boxes**

1. Draw hands to show 7:15.

2.

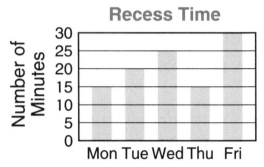

Recess Time

Which day had the longest recess? Circle the best answer.

A. Tuesday   **B.** Friday

C. Wednesday   **D.** Monday

3. Use counters to make a 5-by-3 array. Draw the array.

How many counters in all?

_____ counters

4. Fill in the missing numbers.

614	

	625	

5. Draw or write the names of two things in the classroom that are the shape of a rectangular prism.

6. Write the fraction.

The part shaded = _____

1) MG 1.4   2) SDAP 1.4   3) NS **3.1**
4) SDAP 2.1   5) MG **2.0**   6) NS **4.1**

Record of Our Jumps

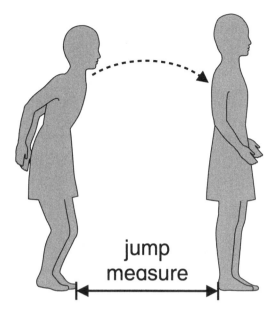

jump
measure

Place a penny or other marker (or make a dot with chalk) where the
Jumper's back heel lands. Measure from the starting line to the marker.
The jumps are measured to the nearest centimeter.

1. Record two of your jumps. Measure jumps to the nearest centimeter.

   First try: _____ centimeters

   Second try: _____ centimeters

2. My longer jump was _____ centimeters.

3. A middle value of jumps for our class is _____ centimeters.

LESSON 7·6 Record of Our Arm Spans

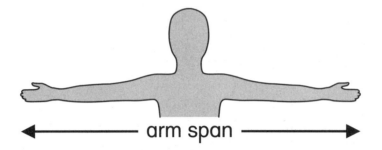

arm span

1. My arm span is _____ inches.

2. A middle value (median) of arm spans for our class is _____ inches.

MG 1.0, **1.3**; SDAP **1.0**

Date _____ Time _____

---

1. Show five possible ways to make 40¢.

2. 2 bunches of bananas. Each bunch has 5 bananas. How many bananas in all?

_____ bananas

Complete the diagram.

bunches	bananas per bunch	bananas in all

---

3. What is the temperature? Fill in the circle next to the best answer.

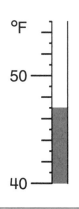

Ⓐ 43°

Ⓑ 53°

Ⓒ 46°

Ⓓ 47°

4. Which number is the most popular (the mode)?

Unit
minutes of homework

_____

12, 12, 12, 14, 15, 16, 16

MRB
45

---

5. Make a ballpark estimate. Then solve the problem.
Ballpark estimate:

_____

    52
  − 29
  _____

MRB
31–33

6. Write <, >, or = in the box.

$\frac{1}{3}$ ☐ $\frac{2}{3}$

MRB
12–15

LESSON 7·7 The Lengths of Objects

Reminder: *in.* means *inches; cm* means *centimeters*

Measure each item to the nearest inch.
Measure each item to the nearest centimeter.
Record your answers in the blank spaces.

1. pencil

about _____ in.

about _____ cm

2. screwdriver

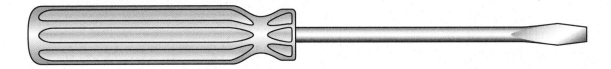

about _____ in.

about _____ cm

3. pen

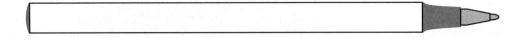

about _____ in.

about _____ cm

LESSON 7·7   The Lengths of Objects continued

4. bolt

about _____ in.

about _____ cm

5. dandelion leaf

about _____ in.

about _____ cm

6. List the objects in order from shortest to longest.

_____

_____

_____

_____

_____

Math Boxes

1. Draw hands to show 4:15.

2.   **Books Read**

Number of Books

		X	
		X	
X		X	
X		X	X
X		X	X
X	X	X	X
X	X	X	X

Juan   Lilly   Grace   Terell

Who read the most books
(maximum)? _____

Who read the least books
(minimum)? _____

3. There are 6 rooms. Each room
has 4 windows. How many

windows in all? _____ windows

Draw an array.

4. Fill in the missing numbers.

892	
	903

5. Here is a picture of a pyramid.
What is the shape of one of

the faces? _____

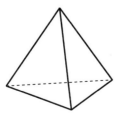

6. Color $\frac{5}{8}$ of the rectangle.

LESSON 7·8   *Soccer Spin* Directions

Materials   ☐ *Math Masters*, pp. 470 and 471

☐ counter

☐ paper clip

☐ pencil

Use a pencil and paper clip to make a spinner.

Players   2

Skill   Predict outcomes of events

Object of the Game   To test the prediction made at the beginning of the game

Directions

1. Players agree upon one spinner to use during the game.

2. Each player chooses a team to cheer for, **Checks** or **Stripes.** (Players can cheer for the same team.) They look at their spinner choice and predict which team will win the game.

3. The game begins with the counter in the center of the soccer field.

4. Players take turns spinning and moving the counter one space toward the goal that comes up on the spinner.

5. The game is over when the counter reaches a goal.

6. Players compare and discuss the results of their predictions. Play two more games using the other two spinners.

Follow-Up

1. Which spinner(s) would you want to use if you were cheering for the **Checks** team? Explain.

2. Which spinner(s) would you want to use if you were cheering for the **Stripes** team? Explain.

LESSON 7·8   Table of Our Arm Spans

Make a table of the arm spans of your classmates.

Arm Span (inches)	Frequency	
	Tallies	Number
	Total =	

LESSON 7·8 Bar Graph of Our Arm Spans

Make a bar graph of the arm spans of your classmates.

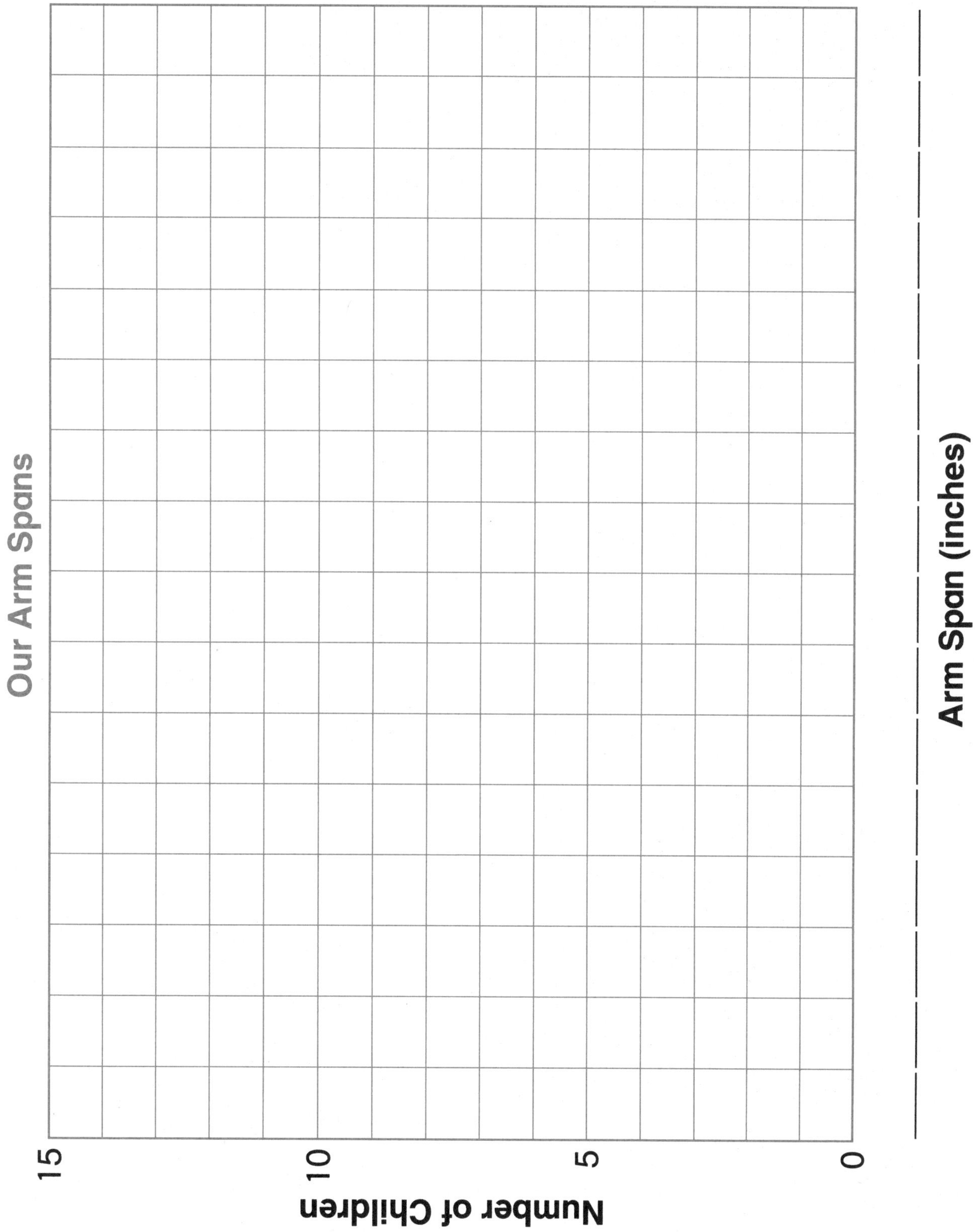

Our Arm Spans

Arm Span (inches)

15

10

5

0

Number of Children

Date _____ Time _____

1. Show five ways to make 45¢.

2. 6 children. Each has 4 stickers. How many stickers in all?

_____ stickers

Complete the multiplication diagram.

children	stickers per child	stickers in all

3. Show 52° on the thermometer.

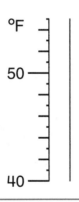

4. Put these numbers in order.

25, 15, 25, 19, 15, 75, 15

_____

Which number is the most popular (the mode)?

_____

5. Write a number model for a ballpark estimate. Solve.

 Unit

Ballpark estimate:

_____

47
− 31

6. Write <, >, or = in the box.

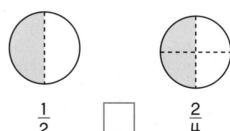

$\frac{1}{2}$ ☐ $\frac{2}{4}$

LESSON 7·9   Math Boxes

1.

What fraction of the triangles are shaded?

 / 5

2. Fill in the box.

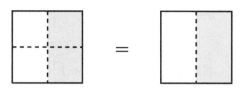

$\dfrac{\square}{4} = \dfrac{1}{2}$

3. Hana has 6 bracelets to wear. 3 of them are made of beads. What fraction of the bracelets are made of beads?

_____

4. Shade $\frac{1}{3}$ of this trapezoid.

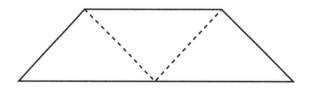

5. Circle $\frac{1}{4}$ of the pennies.

6.

If 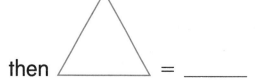 = 1,

then △ = _____

LESSON 8·1 **Equal Parts**

Use a straightedge or Pattern-Block Template.

1. Divide the shape into 2 equal parts. Color 1 part.

   Part colored = $\dfrac{1}{2}$ Part not colored = $\dfrac{\square}{\square}$

   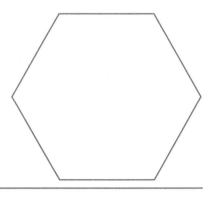

2. Divide the shape into 6 equal parts. Color 1 part.

   Part colored = $\dfrac{\square}{\square}$ Part not colored = $\dfrac{\square}{\square}$

   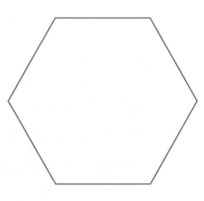

3. Divide the shape into 3 equal parts. Color 2 parts.

   Part colored = $\dfrac{\square}{\square}$ Part not colored = $\dfrac{\square}{\square}$

   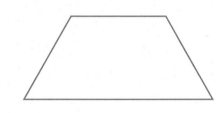

4. Divide the shape into 4 equal parts. Color 2 parts.

   Part colored = $\dfrac{\square}{\square}$ Part not colored = $\dfrac{\square}{\square}$

   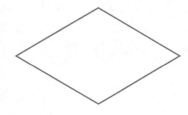

 Number Sense 4.0, **4.2**; Measurement and Geometry **2.2**

Dressing for School

Jerome is deciding what to wear to school today. He has a red shirt, a blue shirt, and a green shirt. He has a black pair of pants, a yellow pair of pants, and an orange pair of pants. How many different outfits can Jerome make? Color the figures below to show the possible shirt and pants combinations that Jerome could wear.

How many possible outfits can Jerome make? _____

LESSON 8·1 **Math Boxes**

---

1. Write fractions.

The part shaded = _____.

The part not shaded = _____.

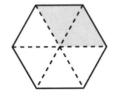

---

2. Use a Pattern-Block Template. Draw a shape that has at least one line of symmetry.

MRB
60

---

3. Complete the table.

in	out
2	1
4	
8	
	5

Rule
$\frac{1}{2}$ of

MRB
100–102

---

4. Show 2 ways to make 50¢. Use Ⓠ, Ⓓ, Ⓝ, and Ⓟ.

MRB
88 89

---

5. Circle the thing you are certain will happen.

You will roll a 7 on a die.

The temperature will be exactly 20°F today.

An hour will pass.

6.

grapes   watermelon

Which item is heavier?

_____

---

1) NS 4.1   2) MR 1.2   3) SDAP 2.2
4) NS 5.1   5) MR 2.0   6) NS 6.1

LESSON 8·2 Pattern-Block Fractions

Use pattern blocks to help you solve each problem.

Use your Pattern-Block Template to show what you did.

Example:

If 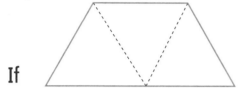 = 1, then  = $\dfrac{1}{3}$.

1. If  = 1, then  = _____.

2. If = 1, then = _____.

3. If 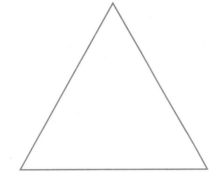 = 1, then  = _____.

4. If = 1, then  = _____.

5. If 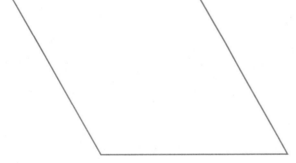 = 1, then = _____.

6. If = 1, then  = _____.

Number Sense 4.0, **4.1**, **4.3**; Measurement and Geometry **2.2**

LESSON 8·2 **Geoboard Fences**

1.

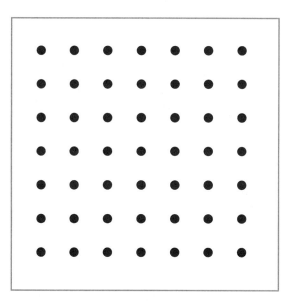

2.

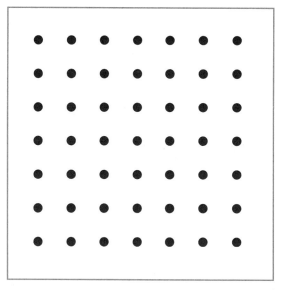

3.

4.

Fence	How many pegs in all?	How many rows of pegs?	How many in each row?
1.			
2.			
3.			
4.			

LESSON 8·2 **Math Boxes**

1. Fill in the missing numbers.

189	
	200

156	
	167

2. 1 hour = _____ minutes

$\frac{1}{2}$ hour = _____ minutes

$\frac{1}{4}$ hour = _____ minutes

MRB
86

3. Put a line under the digit in the ones place.

479   364

1,796   5,079

MRB
10

4. Color $\frac{1}{2}$ of the set green.

5. Measure the length of this line.

_____

about _____ cm

about _____ in.

6. 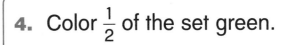 = 1 sq cm

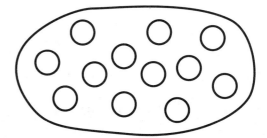

Area = _____ sq cm

MRB
69

1) SDAP 2.1   2) MG 1.4   3) NS 1.1
4) NS 4.2   5) MG 1.3   6) MG 1.0

LESSON 8·3 **Equal Shares**

Use pennies to help you solve the problems.

Circle each person's share.

1. Two people share 10 pennies.
How many pennies does
each person get?

_____ pennies

$\frac{1}{2}$ of 10 pennies = _____ pennies.

---

2. Three people share 9 pennies.
How many pennies does each
person get?

_____ pennies

$\frac{1}{3}$ of 9 pennies = _____ pennies.

$\frac{2}{3}$ of 9 pennies = _____ pennies.

---

3. Four people share
12 pennies.
How many pennies does
each person get?

_____ pennies

$\frac{1}{4}$ of 12 pennies = _____ pennies.

$\frac{3}{4}$ of 12 pennies = _____pennies.

LESSON 8·3 **Fractions of Sets**

A fraction is given in each problem. Color that fraction of the checkers red.

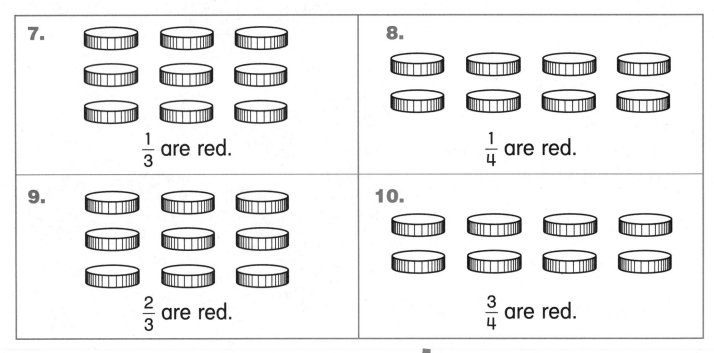

1.

$\frac{1}{5}$ are red.

2.

$\frac{2}{3}$ are red.

3.

$\frac{3}{4}$ are red.

4.

$\frac{4}{6}$ are red.

5.

$\frac{1}{2}$ are red.

6.

$\frac{0}{7}$ are red.

Try This

7.

$\frac{1}{3}$ are red.

8.

$\frac{1}{4}$ are red.

9.

$\frac{2}{3}$ are red.

10.

$\frac{3}{4}$ are red.

Number Sense **4.2**; Mathematical Reasoning 1.2

LESSON 8·3 **Equal Parts**

Use a straightedge or Pattern-Block Template.

1. Divide the shape into 2 equal parts. Color 1 part.

   Part colored = $\dfrac{\Box}{\Box}$ Part not colored = $\dfrac{\Box}{\Box}$

2. Divide the shape into 3 equal parts. Color 1 part.

   Part colored = $\dfrac{\Box}{\Box}$ Part not colored = $\dfrac{\Box}{\Box}$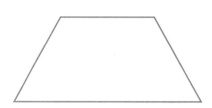

3. Divide the shape into 4 equal parts. Color 2 parts.

   Part colored = $\dfrac{\Box}{\Box}$ Part not colored = $\dfrac{\Box}{\Box}$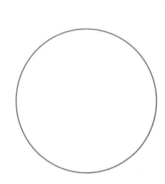

4. Divide the shape into 4 equal parts. Color 3 parts.

   Part colored = $\dfrac{\Box}{\Box}$ Part not colored = $\dfrac{\Box}{\Box}$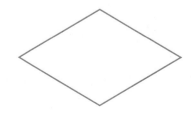

LESSON
8·3   **Math Boxes**

---

1. Color $\frac{1}{4}$ blue. Color $\frac{1}{4}$ yellow. Color $\frac{1}{2}$ red.

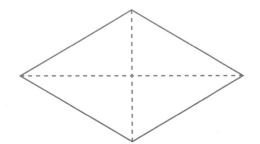

2. Circle the figure that has only one line of symmetry. Draw the line of symmetry.

MRB
60

---

3. Complete the table.

Rule 1 yd = 3 ft	yd	ft
	2	
		9
	5	
		30

4. Show 1 way to make $1.28. Use Ⓠ, Ⓓ, Ⓝ, and Ⓟ.

MRB
88–90

---

5. Circle the event that is likely to happen.

You will fly to the center of the earth.

You will have homework.

You will eat a rock.

6. Which unit makes sense? Choose the best answer.

A can of soup may weigh:

⬭ 8 ounces

⬭ 8 cups

⬭ 8 pounds

⬭ 8 feet

---

1) NS 4.1   2) MR 1.2   3) SDAP 2.2
4) NS 5.1   5) MR 2.0   6) NS 6.1

LESSON 8·4 **Math Boxes**

---

1. Fill in the missing numbers.

	1,217	

2. _____ months = 1 year

_____ months = $\frac{1}{2}$ year

_____ months = $\frac{1}{4}$ year

_____ months = 2 years

---

3. Circle the digits in the hundreds place.

1 2 8   9 7 2   4 6 3

2, 4 6 5   3, 0 9 1

6 6, 2 5 0

4. There are 9 dinosaurs. 3 are plant eaters. Which fraction shows how many are plant eaters? Fill in the circle next to the best answer.

Ⓐ $\frac{9}{3}$ Ⓒ $\frac{1}{2}$

Ⓑ $\frac{3}{9}$ Ⓓ $\frac{2}{3}$

---

5. Draw a triangle. Measure each side to the nearest inch.

about ___ in.

about ___ in.

about ___ in.

6. Count the squares to find the area.

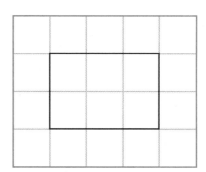

Area = ___ sq cm

LESSON 8·4 Equivalent Fractions

Do the following:

◆ Use the circles that you cut out of *Math Masters,* page 239.

◆ Cut these circles apart along the dashed lines.

◆ Glue the cutout pieces onto the circles on this page and the next, as directed.

◆ Write the missing numerators to complete the equivalent fractions.

1. Cover $\frac{1}{2}$ of the circle with fourths.

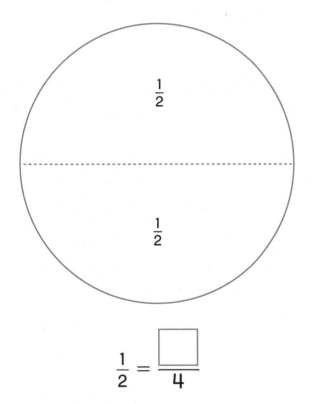

$$\frac{1}{2} = \frac{\square}{4}$$

2. Cover $\frac{1}{4}$ of the circle with eighths.

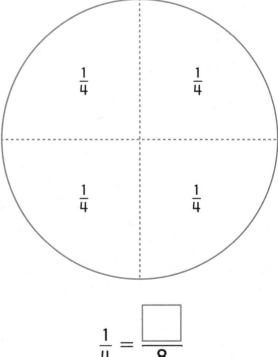

$$\frac{1}{4} = \frac{\square}{8}$$

Number Sense 4.0, 4.1, 4.3; Mathematical Reasoning 1.2

LESSON 8·4   **Equivalent Fractions** *continued*

3. Cover $\frac{2}{4}$ of the circle with eighths.

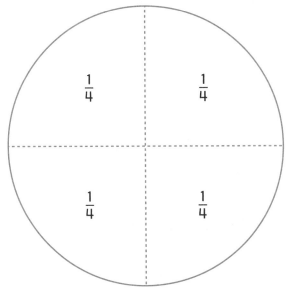

$$\frac{2}{4} = \frac{\Box}{8}$$

4. Cover $\frac{1}{2}$ of the circle with sixths.

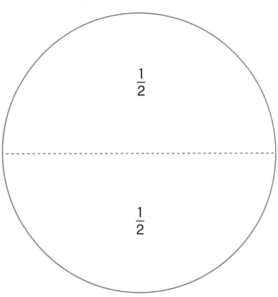

$$\frac{1}{2} = \frac{\Box}{6}$$

5. Cover $\frac{1}{3}$ of the circle with sixths.

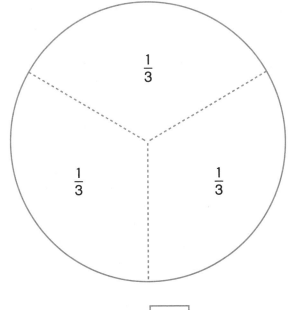

$$\frac{1}{3} = \frac{\Box}{6}$$

6. Cover $\frac{2}{3}$ of the circle with sixths.

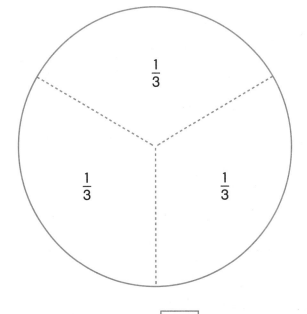

$$\frac{2}{3} = \frac{\Box}{6}$$

LESSON 8·5 *Equivalent Fractions Game* Directions

Materials □ 32 Fraction Cards (2 sets cut from *Math Journal 2*, Activity Sheets 5 and 6)

Players 2

Skill Match equivalent fraction cards

Object of the Game To have the most cards

Directions

1. Mix the Fraction Cards and put them in a stack with the picture sides (the sides with the strips) facedown.

2. Turn the top card over so the picture side faces up. Put it on the table near the stack of cards.

3. Take turns with your partner. When it is your turn, take the top card from the stack. Turn it over and put it on the table. Try to match this card with a picture-side-up card on the table. (If there are no other picture-side-up cards on the table, turn over the next card on the stack and put it on the table.)

4. Look for a match. If two cards match, take both of them. If there is a match that you don't see, the other player can take the matching cards. If there is no match, your turn is over.

5. The game ends when each card has been matched with another card. The player who took more cards wins the game.

Example:

1. The top card is turned over. The picture shows $\frac{4}{6}$.

2. Li turns over the next card. It shows $\frac{2}{3}$. This matches $\frac{4}{6}$. Li takes both cards.

3. Carlos turns over the top card on the stack. It shows $\frac{6}{8}$. Carlos turns over the next card. It shows $\frac{0}{4}$. There is no match. Carlos places $\frac{0}{4}$ next to $\frac{6}{8}$.

4. Li turns over the top card on the stack.

Number Sense 4.0; Number Sense **4.1**

LESSON 8·5   *Equivalent Fractions Game* **Directions** *continued*

Another Version

1. Mix the Fraction Cards and put them in a stack with the picture sides facedown.

2. Turn the top card over so the picture side faces up. Put it on the table with the picture side faceup.

3. Players take turns. When it is your turn, take the top card from the stack, but do *not* turn it over. Keep the picture side down. Try to match the fraction on the card with one of the picture-side-up cards on the table.

4. If you find a match, turn your card over. Check that your match is correct by comparing the two pictures. If your match is correct, take both cards.

   If there is no match, place your card next to the other cards, picture side faceup. Your turn is over. If the other player can find a match, he or she can take the matching cards.

5. If there are no picture cards showing when Player 2 begins his or her turn, take the top card from the stack. Place it on the table with the picture side showing. Then Player 2 takes the next card in the stack and doesn't turn that card over.

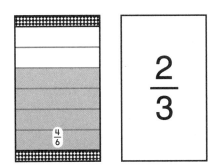

Marta thinks these two cards are a matching pair.

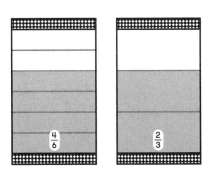

Marta checks that her match is correct by comparing the pictures of the fractions.

LESSON 8·5   Fractions of Collections

Use pennies to help you solve the problems.

1. Five people share 15 pennies.

    How many pennies does each person get? _____ pennies

    $\frac{1}{5}$ of 15 pennies = _____ pennies.

    $\frac{2}{5}$ of 15 pennies = _____ pennies.

2. Six people share 12 pennies.

    How many pennies does each person get? _____ pennies

    $\frac{1}{6}$ of 12 pennies = _____ pennies.

    $\frac{4}{6}$ of 12 pennies = _____ pennies.

3. Four people share 16 pennies.

    How many pennies does each person get? _____ pennies

    $\frac{1}{4}$ of 16 pennies = _____ pennies.

    $\frac{4}{4}$ of 16 pennies = _____ pennies.

    $\frac{2}{4}$ of 16 pennies = _____ pennies.

    $\frac{3}{4}$ of 16 pennies = _____ pennies.

    $\frac{0}{4}$ of 16 pennies = _____ pennies.

Number Sense 4.0, **4.2**, **4.3**

LESSON 8·5   Fractions of Collections *continued*

Color the fractions of circles blue.

---

4. $\frac{3}{5}$ are blue.

5. $\frac{1}{2}$ are blue.

---

6. $\frac{1}{3}$ are blue.

7. $\frac{2}{3}$ are blue.

---

8. $\frac{3}{5}$ are blue.

9. $\frac{3}{4}$ are blue.

Try This

10. $\frac{3}{8}$ are blue.

11. $\frac{2}{6}$ are blue.

LESSON 8·5 **Math Boxes**

---

1. **Scores on a 5-Word Spelling Test**

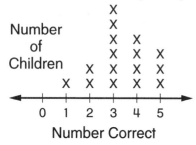

What score did the most children get (the *mode*)? _____

MRB 41

---

2. Circle $\frac{1}{5}$ of the nickels.

---

3. Find the arrow rules.

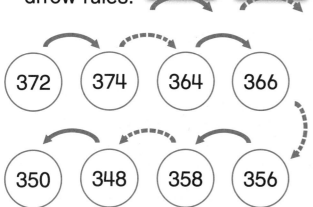

372   374   364   366

350   348   358   356

---

4. Complete the diagram.

Quantity
64

Quantity
28

_____ **Difference**

Write a number model.

_____

MRB 110 111

---

5. Draw a line segment $4\frac{1}{2}$ cm long.

Now draw a line segment 2 cm longer.

MRB 64

---

6. Measure each side of the triangle to the nearest inch. Find the perimeter.

The perimeter is

_____ inches.

MRB 68

---

1) SDAP 1.3   2) NS 4.2   3) SDAP 2.1
4) AF 1.2   5) MG 1.3   6) MG 1.0

LESSON 8·6   *Fraction Top-It* Directions

Use your Fraction Cards. List all the fractions that are:

less than $\frac{1}{2}$. _____

more than $\frac{1}{2}$. _____

the same as $\frac{1}{2}$. _____

Fraction Top-It

Materials   ☐ 32 Fraction Cards (2 sets cut from
                    Math Journal 2, Activity Sheets 5 and 6)

Players   2

Skill   Compare fractions

Object of the Game   To have the most cards

Directions

1. Mix the Fraction Cards and put them in a stack so all the picture sides (the sides with the strips) are facedown.

2. Each player turns over a card from the top of the stack. Players compare the shaded parts of their cards. The player with the larger (higher) fraction takes both cards.

3. If the shaded parts are equal, the fractions are equivalent. Each player turns over another card. The player with the larger fraction takes all the cards from both plays.

4. The game ends when all the cards have been taken from the stack. The player who took more cards wins.

$$\boxed{\frac{1}{2}} \quad \frac{1}{2} \text{ is greater than } \frac{1}{3}. \quad \boxed{\frac{1}{3}}$$

LESSON 8·6 ***Fraction Top-It Directions*** *continued*

Another Version

1. Mix the Fraction Cards and put them in a stack so all the picture sides (the sides with the strips) are facedown.

2. Each player takes a card from the top of the stack but does *not* turn it over.

3. Players take turns. When it is your turn, compare the fractions on the two cards. Say one of the following:

   ◆ My fraction is more than your fraction.

   ◆ My fraction is less than your fraction.

   ◆ The fractions are equivalent.

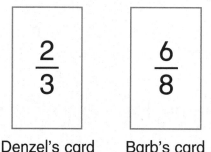

Denzel's card   Barb's card

Denzel says that his fraction is less than Barb's fraction.

4. Turn the cards over and compare the shaded parts. If you were correct, take both cards. If you were not correct, the other player takes both cards.

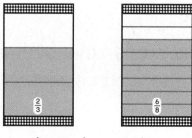

Denzel's card   Barb's card

Less of Denzel's card is shaded: $\frac{2}{3}$ is less than $\frac{6}{8}$. Denzel takes both cards.

Number Sense **4.1**; Number Sense **4.2**

LESSON
8·6   **Math Boxes**

---

1. Fill in the missing numbers.

992	
	1,003

2. There are

_____ minutes in an hour.

_____ hours in a day.

_____ days in a week.

_____ weeks in a year.

---

3. 368

The value of 3 is _____.

The value of 6 is _____.

The value of 8 is _____.

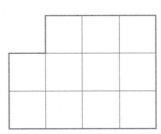
MRB
10

4. Draw hats on $\frac{1}{3}$ of the smiley faces.

---

5. Fill in the circle next to the best answer. A school bus is about:

Ⓐ 180 cm long.

Ⓑ 18 m long.

Ⓒ 18 in long.

Ⓓ 180 m long.

6. ☐ = 1 sq cm

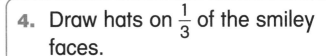

Area = _____ sq cm

MRB
69

Date _____   Time _____

LESSON 8·7 Fraction Number Stories

Solve these number stories. To help, you can use pennies or other counters, or you can draw pictures.

1. Mark has 4 shirts to wear. 3 of them have short sleeves. What fraction of the shirts have short sleeves?

_____

2. 8 birds are sitting on a tree branch. 6 of the birds are sparrows. What fraction of the birds are sparrows?

_____

3. June has 15 fish in her fish tank. $\frac{1}{3}$ of the fish are guppies. How many guppies does she have?

_____

Try This

4. Sam ate $\frac{0}{5}$ of a candy bar. How much of the candy bar did he eat?

_____

5. If you were thirsty, would you rather have $\frac{2}{2}$ of a carton of milk or $\frac{4}{4}$ of that same carton? Explain.

_____

_____

_____

_____

Number Sense 4.0, 4.2; Mathematical Reasoning 2.0

Date _____   Time _____

---

1.   **Baskets Made by 2nd Graders**

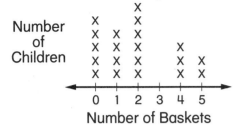

What was the most frequent number of baskets made (the *mode*)? _____

 MRB 41

2. What fraction of dots is circled? Circle the best answer.

A $\frac{1}{2}$

B $\frac{1}{4}$

C $\frac{1}{3}$

D $\frac{2}{4}$

---

3. Fill in the missing numbers.

4. Complete the diagram. Then write a number model.

Quantity
82

Quantity
39

_____ **Difference**

_____

 MRB 110 111

---

5. Draw a line segment that is 6 cm long. Divide the line segment into 3 equal parts.

Each part = _____ cm

MRB 64

6. Measure each side to the nearest cm. Find the perimeter.

The perimeter is _____ cm.

 MRB 68

---

1. Circle. How much does a can of juice hold?

1 ounce

1 gallon

36 liters

12 ounces

2. Draw a square with a perimeter of 8 cm.

Remember: The sides of a square are equal.

MRB
68

---

3. Draw a rectangle. Measure each side to the nearest cm.

about _____ cm

about _____ cm

about _____ cm

about _____ cm

4. Measure the length of this line.

_____

about _____ cm

about _____ in.

---

5. Match the items to the weights.

1 cat   1 ounce

3 envelopes   1 pound

1 book   7 pounds

6. ☐ = 1 sq cm

☐☐☐☐

Area = _____ sq cm

MRB
69

---

1) NS 6.1   2) MR 1.1   3) MG 1.3
4) MG 1.3   5) NS 6.1   6) MG 1.0

LESSON 9·1 ## Yards

Materials ☐ yardstick

Directions

Record each step in the table below.

1. Choose a distance.

2. Estimate the distance in yards.

3. Use a yardstick to measure the distance to the nearest yard. Compare this measurement to your estimate.

Distance I Estimated and Measured	My Estimate	My Yardstick Measurement
	about _____ yards	about _____ yards
	about _____ yards	about _____ yards
	about _____ yards	about _____ yards
	about _____ yards	about _____ yards
	about _____ yards	about _____ yards

Possible Outcomes

LESSON 9·1

Solve the problem.

Your teacher placed 5 buttons in a bag. One button is a white square, 2 buttons are round and black, and 2 buttons are round and white.

Your teacher wants you to pull two buttons out of the bag while keeping your eyes shut. Draw a picture of all the button combinations that you could pull out of the bag.

How many different ways are there to pull two buttons out of the bag?

_____

Mathematical Reasoning 1.2

LESSON 9·1 **Math Boxes**

---

1. Make a square array with 25 pennies. How many pennies are in each row?

_____ pennies

---

2. Write <, >, or =.

$4 + 5 + 6$ _____ $3 + 5 + 7$

$7 + 5 + 9$ _____ $6 + 6 + 8$

$2 + 11 + 4$ _____ $7 + 1 + 9$

$15 + 7 + 5$ _____ $9 + 9 + 9$

---

3. Circle the parallel lines.

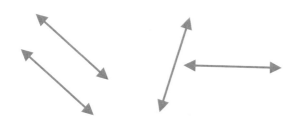

4.

246 228 273
209 298

Unit
yards

The median number of yards is _____.

---

5. Use your Pattern-Block Template. Trace a shape and draw 1 line of symmetry.

---

6. Count by quarters to $3.00.

$0.50, _____, _____,

_____, _____, _____,

_____, _____, _____,

_____, _____

LESSON 9·2 Units of Linear Measure

Materials □ 12-inch ruler   □ 10-centimeter ruler

Directions

1. Measure the length of two objects or distances.

2. First measure to the nearest foot. Measure again to the nearest inch.

3. Then measure to the nearest decimeter. Measure again to the nearest centimeter.

Object *or* Distance	Nearest Foot	Nearest Inch
	about _____ ft	about _____ in.
	about _____ ft	about _____ in.

Object *or* Distance	Nearest Decimeter	Nearest Centimeter
	about _____ dm	about _____ cm
	about _____ dm	about _____ cm

"What's My Rule?"

4.

Rule

1 ft = 12 in.

ft	in.
1	
2	
	36

5.

Rule

1 m = 100 cm

m	cm
1	
	300
10	

Measurement and Geometry 1.1, 1.2, 1.3

LESSON 9·2   **Math Boxes**

---

1. Fill in the missing numbers.

		1,250
	1,259	
1,268		

---

2. Draw a line segment that is 8 cm long. Now draw a line segment 5 cm shorter.

MRB
50

---

3. Dillon leaped 32 inches. Marcus leaped 27 inches. How many more inches did Dillon leap? _____ inches

Fill in the diagram.

Quantity

Quantity

_____
Difference

MRB
110 111

---

4. What is the chance that you will have two birthdays this year? Choose the best answer.

⬭ unlikely

⬭ likely

⬭ certain

⬭ impossible

---

5. 3 insects. 6 legs per insect. How many legs in all?

_____ legs

Fill in the diagram and write a number model.

insects	legs per insect	legs in all

_____ × _____ = _____

MRB
112 113

---

6. Solve.

_____ pennies = $2.00

_____ nickels = $2.00

_____ dimes = $2.00

_____ quarters = $2.00

LESSON 9·3 Measuring Lengths with a Ruler

Materials   ☐ inch ruler

☐ centimeter ruler

Directions

Work with a partner. Use your ruler to measure the length of each object to the nearest inch and centimeter.

1. large paper clip

about _____ inches long   about _____ centimeters long

2. pencil

about _____ inches long   about _____ centimeters long

3. nail

about _____ inch long   about _____ centimeters long

Try This

Measure to the nearest $\frac{1}{2}$-inch and $\frac{1}{2}$-centimeter.

4. small paper clip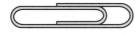

about _____ inches long   about _____ centimeters long

Number Sense 4.0; Measurement and Geometry 1.2, 1.3

LESSON 9·3 **Math Boxes**

---

1. Make a square array with 36 pennies. How many pennies in each row?

_____ pennies

---

2. Complete each number model.

Unit

_____ > 199

372 > _____

_____ < 2,424

5,269 < _____

---

3. Draw a quadrangle. Make 2 sides parallel.

51 55

---

4. 264   246   310
277   301

Unit
meters

Find the median number of meters. Circle the best answer.

A. 264   **B.** 277

C. 301   **D.** 310

46

---

5. Find 2 lines of symmetry.

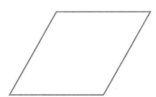

60

---

6. How much in all?

_____

Ⓓ Ⓓ
Ⓠ Ⓠ Ⓠ Ⓝ

$20 $5
$10 $5

88–90

LESSON 9·4 Distance Around and Perimeter

Measure the distance around the following to the nearest centimeter.

1. Your neck: _____ cm

2. Your ankle: _____ cm

Measure the distance around two other objects to the nearest centimeter.

3. Object: _____ Measurement: _____ cm

4. Object: _____ Measurement: _____ cm

Measure each side of the figure to the nearest inch. Write the length next to each side. Then find the perimeter.

5.

Perimeter: _____ inches

Try This

6.

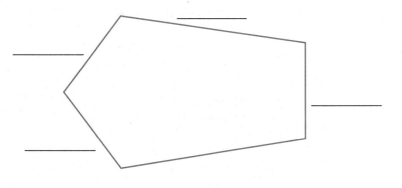

Perimeter: _____ inches

LESSON 9·4 **Math Boxes**

1. Fill in the missing numbers.

1,789	
1,799	

2. Draw a line segment that is $3\frac{1}{2}$ inches long.

Now draw a line segment that is 1 inch shorter.

3. The Jays scored 63 points. The Gulls scored 46 points. How many more points did the Jays score? _____ points

Fill in the diagram.

Quantity

Quantity

_____
Difference

4. What is the chance that you will fly in a spaceship today? Circle your answer.

impossible

certain

likely

unlikely

5. 9 cars. Each has 4 tires. How many tires in all?

cars	tires per car	tires in all

6. Use Ⓟ, Ⓝ, Ⓓ, and Ⓠ. Show $1.79.

LESSON 9·5   **Driving in the West**

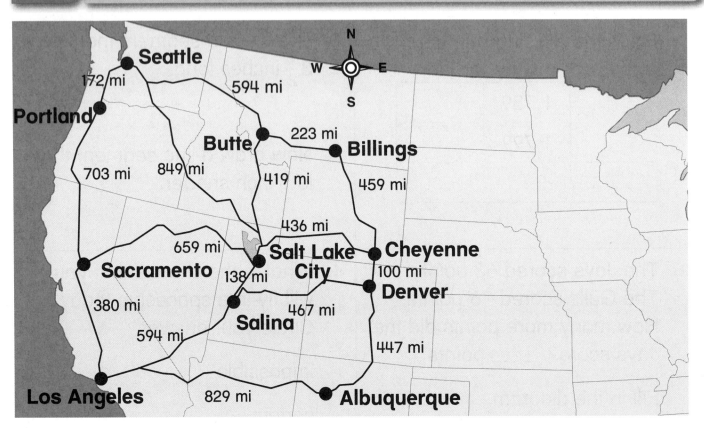

1. What is the shortest route from Seattle to Albuquerque?

   _____

   _____

2. Put a check mark in front of the longer trip.

   _____ Salt Lake City to Billings by way of Butte

   _____ Salt Lake City to Billings by way of Cheyenne

   How much longer is that trip?   about _____ miles longer

Number Sense **2.1**, **2.2**; Measurement and Geometry **1.0**

Addition and Subtraction Practice

Make a ballpark estimate. Solve. Compare your answer to your estimate.

1. Ballpark estimate:

_____

$45 + 68 =$ _____

2. Ballpark estimate:

_____

$143 + 78 =$ _____

3. Ballpark estimate:

_____

$158 + 233 =$ _____

4. Ballpark estimate:

_____

$74 - 49 =$ _____

5. Ballpark estimate:

_____

$133 - 86 =$ _____

6. Ballpark estimate:

_____

$256 - 147 =$ _____

LESSON 9·5 **Math Boxes**

1. Write 5 names for $\frac{1}{2}$. Use your Fraction Cards if you need help.

$\frac{1}{2}$

2. Write even or odd.

126 _____

311 _____

109 _____

430 _____

3. 17 sticks of cheese are shared equally. Each child gets 3 sticks.

How many children are sharing?

_____ children

How many sticks are left over?

_____ sticks

4. Rosita had $0.39 and found $0.57 more. How much does she have now? Estimate your answer and then use partial sums to solve.

Estimate:

_____ + _____ = _____

Answer: _____

5. In Pensacola, Florida, the temperature is 82°F. In Portland, Maine, the temperature is 64°F. What is the difference? Fill in the circle next to the best answer.

Ⓐ 22°F   Ⓑ 17°F

Ⓒ 20°F   Ⓓ 18°F

6. A number has:

7 thousands
8 tens
5 ten-thousands
1 one
0 hundreds

Write the number. _____

1) NS 4.1   2) NS 1.0   3) NS 3.2
4) NS 5.2   5) NS 2.2   6) NS 1.1

LESSON 9·6 **Math Message**

 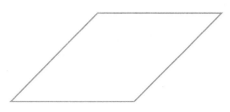 

Estimate: Which shape is the "biggest" (has the largest area)? Circle it.

Think: How might you measure the shapes to find out?

Exploration A: Which Cylinder Holds More?

Which holds more macaroni—the tall and narrow cylinder or the short and wide cylinder?

My prediction: _____

Actual result: _____

Exploration B: Measuring Area

The area of my tracing of the deck of cards is about _____ square centimeters.

The area of my tracing of the deck of cards is about _____ square inches.

I traced _____.

It has an area of about _____.
$$\text{(unit)}$$

LESSON
9·6

Math Boxes

1. Write 5 names in the 90-box.

MRB
16

2. Fill in the missing numbers.

MRB
98 99

3. Solve. Show your work.

$$\begin{array}{r} 27 \\ + 56 \\ \hline \end{array}$$

4.

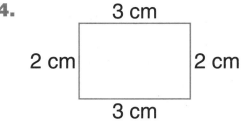

Perimeter = _____ cm

MRB
68

5. Write a number model for a ballpark estimate. Then solve.

Ballpark estimate:

_____

$$\begin{array}{r} 68 \\ + 34 \\ \hline \end{array}$$

MRB
30

6. The total cost is 60¢. You pay with a $1 bill.

How much change do you get?

_____

Show the change using
Ⓠ, Ⓓ, and Ⓝ.

1) NS 1.2   2) SDAP 2.2   3) NS 2.2
4) MG 1.0   5) NS 2.0   6) NS 5.1

LESSON 9·7 Math Boxes

---

1. Draw two ways to show $\frac{2}{3}$.

2. Write 3 even numbers larger than 100.

_____ , _____ , _____

Write 3 odd numbers smaller than 100.

_____ , _____ , _____

MRB
97

---

3. Get 36 counters. Share them equally among 4 children.

How many counters does each child get? _____ counters

How many are left over?

_____ counters

MRB
114 115

4. I have $2.00. Can I buy 4 bags of chips for $0.55 each?

_____

---

5. Solve.

Unit

386 − 40 = _____

_____ = 198 − 60

259 − 40 = _____

_____ = 243 − 20

6. In 43,692, the value of

4 is _____.

3 is _____.

6 is _____.

9 is _____.

2 is _____.

MRB
10 11

LESSON 9·8   Equivalent Units of Capacity

Complete.

U.S. Customary Units of Capacity

_____ pint = 1 cup

1 pint = _____ cups

_____ pints = 1 quart

_____ quarts = 1 half-gallon

_____ half-gallons = 1 gallon

Metric Units of Capacity

1 liter = _____ milliliters

$\frac{1}{2}$ liter = _____ milliliters

1. How many quarts are in 1 gallon? _____ quarts

2. How many cups are in 1 quart? _____ cups

   In a half-gallon? _____ cups   In 1 gallon? _____ cups

3. How many pints are in a half-gallon? _____ pints

   In a gallon? _____ pints

"What's My Rule?"

4.

Rule	qt	pt
1 qt = 2 pt	2	
	3	
		10
	8	

5.

Rule	gal	pt
1 gal = 8 pt	2	
	3	
		40
		80

Measurement and Geometry 1.0, 1.2

LESSON
9·8   **Math Boxes**

1. Write 5 names for 130.

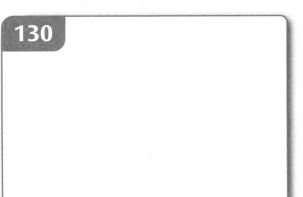

130

MRB
16

2. Fill in the missing numbers.

+9   −4

89

MRB
98 99

3. Solve. Show your work.

49
+ 23

4.

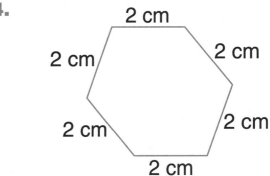

2 cm
2 cm
2 cm
2 cm
2 cm
2 cm

Perimeter = _____ cm

MRB
68

5. Estimate. Then solve.

Estimate:

_____ + _____ = _____

57
+ 48

6. The total cost is $1.50. You pay with a $5 bill. How much change do you get?

Fill in the circle next to the best answer.

Ⓐ $6.50   Ⓑ $2.50

Ⓒ $4.00   Ⓓ $3.50

LESSON 9·9 Weight

Weighing Pennies

Use a spring scale, letter scale, or diet scale to weigh pennies. Find the number of pennies that weigh about 1 ounce.

I found that _____ pennies weigh about 1 ounce.

Which Objects Weigh about the Same?

Work in a small group. Your group will be given several objects that weigh less than 1 pound.

1. Choose two objects. Hold one object in each hand and compare their weights. Try to find two objects that weigh about the same.

   Two objects that weigh about the same:

   _____   _____

2. After everyone in the group has chosen two objects that weigh about the same, weigh all the objects. Record the weights below.

   Object   **Weight** (include unit)

   _____   _____

   _____   _____

   _____   _____

   _____   _____

   _____   _____

Measurement and Geometry 1.0; Statistics, Data Analysis, and Probability 1.1

LESSON 9·9   **Math Boxes**

---

1. Use your Fraction Cards.
Find another name for $\frac{3}{4}$.
Circle the best answer.

A $\frac{1}{2}$ B $\frac{3}{8}$

C $\frac{6}{8}$ D $\frac{2}{3}$

---

2. Write 2 even 4-digit numbers.

_____ _____

Write 2 odd 4-digit numbers.

_____ _____

---

3. Use counters to solve.

18 orange slices are shared equally. Each child gets 4 slices.

How many children are sharing?

_____ children

How many slices are left?

_____ slices

---

4. Fill in the missing amount.

I had 38¢.

I spent _____¢.

I have 15¢ left.

---

5. Solve.

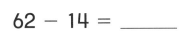
Unit

$22 - 14 =$ _____

$62 - 14 =$ _____

$162 - 14 =$ _____

_____ $= 292 - 14$

_____ $= 402 - 14$

---

6. In 96,527, the value of

5 is _____.

6 is _____.

7 is _____.

2 is _____.

9 is _____.

LESSON 9·10   Math Boxes

---

1. I have 85¢. How many 5¢ pencils can I buy?

_____ pencils

2. 67,248

The value of 8 is _____.

The value of 2 is _____.

The value of 7 is _____.

The value of 6 is _____.

The value of 4 is _____.

3. How much money?

$10 $5

Ⓠ Ⓝ Ⓝ Ⓟ

$_____

4. The total cost of Neena's lunch is $7.50.

She paid with a $10 bill.

How much change will she get?

$ _____

5. Justin had $0.92 and found $0.21 more. How much does he have now? Estimate your answer and then solve.

Estimate:

_____ + _____ = _____

Answer: _____

6. Use Ⓟ, Ⓝ, Ⓓ, and Ⓠ. Show $2.20.

---

1) NS 3.0   2) NS 1.1   3) NS 5.1
4) NS 5.1   5) NS 2.0   6) NS 5.0

Math Boxes

---

1. Double.

25¢ _____

55¢ _____

65¢ _____

85¢ _____

2. 15 children. $\frac{1}{3}$ are boys.

How many are boys? _____

How many are girls? _____

MRB
14

---

3. Count by 1000s.

_____; 2,728; _____;

_____; _____; _____;

_____; _____; _____

4. Solve.

 Unit

$5 + 3 =$ _____

$50 + 30 =$ _____

$$\begin{array}{r} 6 \\ + 3 \\ \hline \end{array} \qquad \begin{array}{r} 60 \\ + 30 \\ \hline \end{array}$$

---

5. Draw a rhombus. Make each side 2 cm long.

6. How many dots are in this 5-by-5 array?

• • • • •
• • • • •
• • • • •
• • • • •
• • • • •

_____ dots in all

MRB
55

LESSON 10·1 Good Buys Poster

Fruit/Vegetables Group

Seedless Grapes
99¢ lb

Carrots
1-lb bag
3/$1.00

Plums
69¢ lb

Oranges
$1.49 lb

Bananas
59¢ lb

Watermelons
$2.99 ea.

Celery
59¢ lb

Meat Group

Pork & Beans
16 oz
2/89¢

Peanut Butter
18-oz jar
$1.29

Ground Beef
$1.99 lb

Chunk Light
Tuna
6.5 oz
69¢

Lunch Meat
1-lb package
$1.39

Milk Group

Gallon
Milk
$2.39

American
Cheese
8 oz
$1.49

6-pack
Yogurt
$2.09

Grain Group

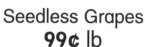
Wheat Bread
16 oz
99¢

Saltines
1 lb
69¢

Hamburger Buns
16 oz
69¢

Miscellaneous Items

Mayonnaise
32 oz
$1.99

Catsup
32 oz
$1.09

Grape Jelly
2-lb jar
$1.69

NS 5.0, **5.1**, **5.2**, 6.0; MR 2.0, 2.2

LESSON 10·1   **Ways to Pay**

Complete Problem 1. For Problems 2 and 3 choose two items from the Good Buys Poster on page 230. List the items and how much they cost in the table below.

For each item:

◆ Count out coins and bills to show several different ways of paying for each item.

◆ Record two ways by drawing coins and bills in the table. Use Ⓠ, Ⓓ, Ⓝ, Ⓟ, and $1.

Example:
You buy 1 pound of bananas. They cost 59¢ a pound. You pay with:
Ⓠ Ⓠ Ⓝ Ⓟ Ⓟ Ⓟ Ⓟ **or** Ⓓ Ⓓ Ⓓ Ⓓ Ⓓ Ⓝ Ⓟ Ⓟ Ⓟ Ⓟ

---

1. You buy *oranges*.

Cost: _____$1.49_____

Pay with _____ or _____

2. You buy _____.

Cost: _____

Pay with _____ or _____

---

3. You buy _____.

Cost: _____

Pay with _____ or _____

Try This

4. You buy _____

and _____.

Cost: _____

Pay with _____ or _____

LESSON 10·2 Word Values

Pretend the letters of the alphabet have the dollar values shown in the table. For example, the letter **g** is worth $7; the letter **v** is worth $22. The word **jet** is worth $10 + $5 + $20 = $35.

	a	b	c	d	e	f	g	h	i	j	k	l	m
Value	$1	$2	$3	$4	$5	$6	$7	$8	$9	$10	$11	$12	$13
	n	o	p	q	r	s	t	u	v	w	x	y	z
Value	$14	$15	$16	$17	$18	$19	$20	$21	$22	$23	$24	$25	$26

1. Which is worth more, **dog** or **cat**? _____

2. Which is worth more, **whale** or **zebra?** _____

3. How much is your first name worth? _____

4. Write 2 spelling words you are trying to learn. Find their values.

   Word: _____ Value: $_____

   Word: _____ Value: $_____

5. What is the cheapest word you can make? It must have at least

   2 letters.

   Word: _____ Value: $_____

6. What is the most expensive word you can make?

   Word: _____ Value: $_____

Try This

7. Think of the letter values as dimes. For example, **m** is worth 13 dimes; **b** is worth 2 dimes. Find out how much each word is worth.

   dog: $_____   cat: $_____   zebra: $_____   whale: $_____

   candy: $_____   your last name: $_____

Number Sense 5.0, 5.1, 5.2

LESSON 10·2 **Math Boxes**

---

1. Write <, >, or =.

1,257 _____ 2,157

7,925 _____ 5,297

10,129 _____ 1,129

MRB 9

---

2. Circle the answer.

$2.88 is closer to:
$2.80   or $2.90

$5.61 is closer to:
$5.60   or $5.70

$1.97 is closer to:
$1.90   or $2.00

---

3. Put the heights in order. Find the median height.

48 44 37 54 39

Unit
inches

_____, _____, _____, _____, _____

The median height is

_____ inches.

MRB 46

---

4. What is the temperature? Circle the best answer.

A. 85°F

B. 86°F

C. 83°F

D. 76°F

---

5. Draw the hour and minute hands to show the time 20 minutes later than 6:15.

What time does the clock show now?

_____:_____

---

6. You have 21 pennies to share equally among 3 children. How many pennies does each child get?

_____ pennies

How many are left over?

_____ pennies

MRB 114 115

LESSON 10·3   Calculator Dollars and Cents

To enter $4.27 into your calculator, press ④ ⨀ ② ⑦.

To enter 35¢ into your calculator, press ⨀ ③ ⑤.

1. Enter $3.58 into your calculator. The display shows _____.

2. Enter the following amounts into your calculator.

   Record what the display shows.
   Don't forget to clear between each entry.

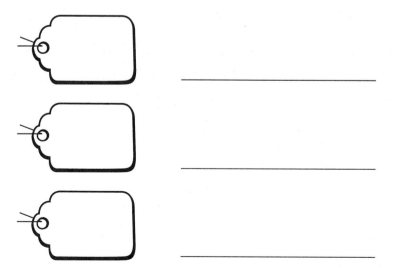

Price	Display
$2.75	_____
$1.69	_____
$12.32	_____

Make up prices that are more than $1.00.

	_____
	_____
	_____

3. Enter 68¢ into your calculator. The display shows _____.

Number Sense 5.1, 5.2

LESSON 10·3 **Calculator Dollars and Cents** *continued*

4. Enter the following amounts into your calculator.
   Record what you see in the display.

   Price   **Display**

   $0.10   _____

   $0.26   _____

   $0.09   _____

   Make up prices that are less than $1.00.

                  _____

                  _____

                  _____

5. Use your calculator to add $1.55 and $0.25.

   What does the display show? _____

   Explain what happened. _____

   _____

LESSON 10·3   *Pick-a-Coin* Directions

Materials   ☐ 1 die   ☐ calculator for each player

☐ *Pick-a-Coin* record table for each player
(*Math Journal 2*, p. 237 or *Math Masters*, p. 469)

Players   2 to 4

Skill   Add dollar bill and coin combinations

Object of the Game   To add the largest value

Summary

Players roll a die. The numbers that come up are used as numbers of coins and dollar bills. Players try to make collections of coins and bills with the largest value.

Directions

Take turns. When it is your turn, roll the die five times. After each roll, record the number that comes up on the die in any one of the empty cells in the row for that turn on your record table. Then use a calculator to find the total amount for that turn. Record the total in the table.

After four turns, use your calculator to add the four totals. The player with the largest Grand Total wins.

Example: On his first turn, Brian rolled 4, 2, 4, 1, and 6.
He filled in his record table like this:

Pick-a-Coin Record Table						
	Ⓟ	Ⓝ	Ⓓ	Ⓠ	$1	**Total**
1st turn	2	1	4	4	6	$ 7 . 47
2nd turn						$ __ . ____
3rd turn						$ __ . ____
4th turn						$ __ . ____
				Grand Total		$ __ . ____

Number Sense 5.0, **5.1**, **5.2**

LESSON 10·3   *Pick-a-Coin* Record Tables

	Ⓟ	Ⓝ	Ⓓ	Ⓠ	$1	Total
1st turn						$___ . _____
2nd turn						$___ . _____
3rd turn						$___ . _____
4th turn						$___ . _____
					Grand Total	$___ . _____

	Ⓟ	Ⓝ	Ⓓ	Ⓠ	$1	Total
1st turn						$___ . _____
2nd turn						$___ . _____
3rd turn						$___ . _____
4th turn						$___ . _____
					Grand Total	$___ . _____

	Ⓟ	Ⓝ	Ⓓ	Ⓠ	$1	Total
1st turn						$___ . _____
2nd turn						$___ . _____
3rd turn						$___ . _____
4th turn						$___ . _____
					Grand Total	$___ . _____

LESSON 10·3   Finding the Median

One way to find the median:
- ◆ Circle the tally marks.

Example:

Arm Span (inches)	Frequency	
	Tallies	Number
42	Ⓘ Ⓘ	2
43		
44	Ⓘ	1
45		
46	Ⓘ / / Ⓘ	4
47	Ⓘ Ⓘ	2
48		
49	Ⓘ	1
Total		

Median ____46____ inches

Another way:
- ◆ Order the arm-span data in inches.

Example:

4̶2̶, 4̶2̶, 4̶4̶, 4̶6̶, 46, 46, 4̶6̶, 4̶7̶, 4̶7̶, 4̶9̶

Median ____46____ inches

Find the median in two ways. Show your work.

1. One way:

Number of Siblings	Frequency	
	Tallies	Number
6		
5	/	1
4		
3	/ / / /	4
2	/ /	2
1	/ / / /	4
0	/	1
Total		12

Median _____ siblings

2. Another way:

0 1 1 1 1 2 2 3 3 3 3 5

Median _____ siblings

Statistics, Data Analysis, and Probability 1.1, 1.3

LESSON 10·3 Math Boxes

1. _____ pennies = $3.00

_____ nickels = $3.00

_____ dimes = $3.00

_____ quarters = $3.00

2. Count 20 pennies.

$\frac{1}{2}$ = _____ pennies

$\frac{1}{4}$ = _____ pennies

$\frac{1}{5}$ = _____ pennies

3. Complete the frames.

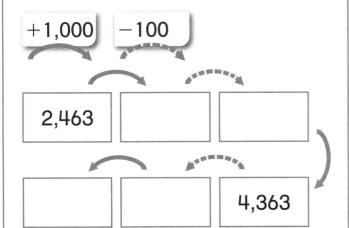

$+1{,}000$ -100

| 2,463 | | |

| | | 4,363 |

4. Solve.

Unit

$9 - 5 =$ _____

_____ $= 90 - 50$

$900 - 500 =$ _____

_____ $= 9{,}000 - 5{,}000$

5. Match.

5 ft   3 yd

24 in.   60 in.

9 ft   2 ft

6. Draw an 8-by-4 array.

How many in all? _____

MRB
67

Then-and-Now Poster

Now

Crackers
1 lb
$2.49

Grape Jelly
2 lb
$2.29

20-Inch Girl's Bicycle
$119.99

Harmonica
Ten Double Holes
$17.50

Raisins
1 lb
$2.39

Cheddar Cheese
8 oz ($\frac{1}{2}$ lb)
$2.99

Catsup
32 oz/1 qt
$2.79

Child's Wagon
Medium Size—15$\frac{1}{2}$" × 34"
$47.99

1897

Crackers
1 lb
6¢

Grape Jelly
2 lb
28¢

20-Inch Girl's Bicycle
$29.00

Harmonica
Ten Double Holes
45¢

Cheddar Cheese
$\frac{1}{2}$ lb
6¢

Raisins
1 lb
10¢

Catsup
32 oz/1 qt
25¢

Child's Wagon
Large Size —15" × 30"
$1.65

Number Sense 5.0, **5.1**, **5.2**; Mathematical Reasoning 1.1, 2.0

LESSON 10·4   **Then-and-Now Prices**

Use your calculator.

1. How much did a 20-inch bicycle cost in 1897? _____

   How much does it cost now? _____

   How much more does it cost now? _____

2. How much more does a pound of cheese cost now

   than it did in 1897? _____

3. In 1897, raisins were packed in cartons. Each carton
   contained 24 one-pound boxes. How much did a

   24-pound carton cost then? _____

   How much would it cost now? _____

4. Which item had the biggest price increase from then to now?

   _____ had the biggest price increase.

   How much more does it cost now? _____

5. Our Own Problems about Then-and-Now:

   _____

   _____

   _____

   _____

   _____

   _____

LESSON 10·4 **Math Boxes**

1. Write <, >, or =.

1,292 + 10 _____ 1,285 + 15

3,791 + 7 _____ 3,799 + 7

5,020 + 100 _____ 5,125 + 25

MRB 9

2. Fill in the blanks to estimate the total cost.

$2.43 + $0.39 is about

_____ + _____ = _____

$0.88 + $0.67 is about

_____ + _____ = _____

3. Arrange the numbers in order. Find the median.

98 56 143 172 81

_____, _____, _____,

_____, _____

The median is _____.

MRB 46

4. Show 55°F.

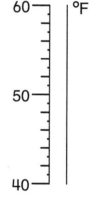

5. It is 6:15. Draw the hour and minute hands to show the time 15 minutes later.

What time does the clock show?

___:___

6. Use counters to solve.

35 blocks are shared equally among 3 children. How many blocks does each child get?

_____ blocks

How many blocks are left over?

_____ blocks

MRB 114 115

1) NS 1.3   2) NS 6.0   3) SDAP 1.3
4) MG 1.0   5) MG 1.4   6) NS 3.2

LESSON 10·5 Estimating and Buying Food

Choose items to buy from the Good Buys Poster on journal page 230.
For each purchase:

◆ Record the items on the sales slip.

◆ Write the price of each item on the sales slip.

◆ Estimate the total cost and record it.

◆ Your partner then uses a calculator to find the exact total cost and
writes it on the sales slip.

Purchase 1	**Price**
Items:	
_____	$ ____ . ____
_____	$ ____ . ____
Estimated cost: about	$ __1__ . __60__
Exact total cost:	$ __1__ . __58__
Purchase 2	**Price**
Items:	
_____	$ ____ . ____
_____	$ ____ . ____
Estimated cost: about	$ ____ . ____
Exact total cost:	$ ____ . ____
Purchase 3	**Price**
Items:	
_____	$ ____ . ____
_____	$ ____ . ____
Estimated cost: about	$ ____ . ____
Exact total cost:	$ ____ . ____

LESSON 10·5   **Math Boxes**

---

1. Show $1.73 in two different ways. Use Ⓟ, Ⓝ, Ⓓ, and Ⓠ.

_____

_____

_____

_____

2. Draw a picture of 10 children.

$\frac{1}{2}$ play ball. How many? _____

$\frac{3}{10}$ jump rope. How many? _____

$\frac{1}{5}$ skate. How many? _____

---

3. Fill in the rule and the missing numbers.

Rule

in	out
1,342	2,342
3,019	4,019
4,650	
	6,700

4. Solve.

Unit

km

$6 + 5 =$ _____

$60 + 50 =$ _____

$600 + 500 =$ _____

$6,000 + 5,000 =$ _____

---

5. Write <, >, or =.

1 qt _____ 1 pt

3 c _____ 1 gal

1 qt _____ 4 c

1 gal _____ 5 pt

6. There are 3 drink boxes per pack. How many packs are needed to serve 25 second graders and 2 teachers one drink box each? Draw an array. Circle the best answer.

_____ packs are needed.

A. 30   **B.** 8   **C.** 9   **D.** 10

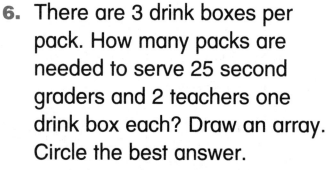

---

1) NS 5.0   2) NS 4.2   3) AF 1.3
4) NS 1.0   5) MG 1.0   6) NS 3.2

LESSON 10·6   **Math Boxes**

---

1. What number is shown by the blocks?

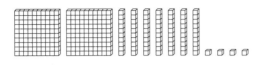

_____

MRB
11

---

2. Joe has $1.00 and spends 65¢. How much change will he get?

_____

---

3. What is the temperature?

_____ °F

Is it warm or cold outside?

_____

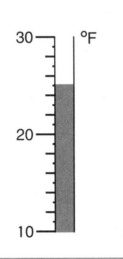

°F
30 —
20 —
10 —

---

4. You buy some stickers for $1.89. Show 2 ways to pay. Use Ⓟ, Ⓝ, Ⓓ, Ⓠ, and $1.

---

5. Write the names of 3 objects that are shaped like cylinders.

_____

_____

_____

MRB
57

---

6. How many stars in all?

★ ★ ★ ★ ★
★ ★ ★ ★ ★
★ ★ ★ ★ ★

_____ stars

Fill in the multiplication diagram.

rows	stars per row	stars in all

MRB
112–113

LESSON 10·6   Making Change

Work with a partner. Use your tool-kit coins and bills. One of you is the shopper. The other is the clerk.

The shopper does the following:

◆ Chooses one item from each food group on the Good Buys Poster on journal page 230.

◆ Lists these items on the Good Buys sales slip in the shopper's journal on page 247.

◆ Writes the cost of each item on the sales slip.

◆ Estimates the total cost of all the items and writes it on the sales slip.

◆ Pays with a $10 bill.

◆ Estimates the change and writes it on the sales slip.

The clerk does the following:

◆ Uses a calculator to find the exact total cost.

◆ Writes the exact total cost on the sales slip.

◆ Gives the shopper change by counting up.

◆ Writes the exact change from $10.00 on the sales slip.

Change roles and repeat.

Number Sense 5.0, 5.1, 6.0

LESSON 10·6 Making Change *continued*

The Good Buys Store Sales Slip

	Item	Cost
Fruit/vegetables group	_____	$ ___ . ___
Grain group	_____	$ ___ . ___
Meat group	_____	$ ___ . ___
Milk group	_____	$ ___ . ___
Miscellaneous items	_____	$ ___ . ___
Estimated total cost		$ ___ . ___
Estimated change from $10.00		$ ___ . ___
Exact total cost		$ ___ . ___
Exact change from $10.00		$ ___ . ___

LESSON 10·7 The Area of My Handprint

The area of each ⬜ is 1 square centimeter. Other ways to write *square centimeter* are sq cm and cm^2.

The area of my handprint is _____ square centimeters, or _____ sq cm.

Mathematical Reasoning 1.2

LESSON 10·7 The Area of My Footprint

The area of each ☐ is 1 square centimeter. Other ways to write *square centimeter* are sq cm and cm².

The area of my footprint is _____ square centimeters, or _____ sq cm.

LESSON 10·7   Worktables

Use a Pattern-Block Template to draw each of the different-size and different-shape worktables you made. Write the name of each shape next to your drawing.

LESSON 10·7   **Geoboard Dot Paper**

1.

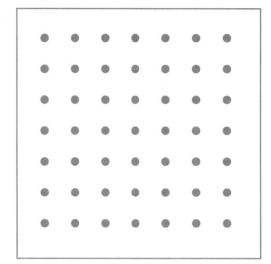

2.

3.

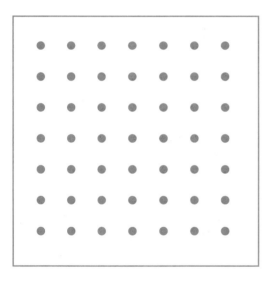

4.

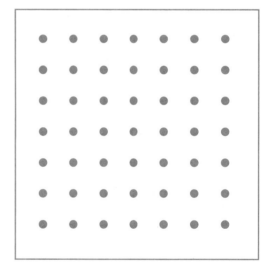

5.

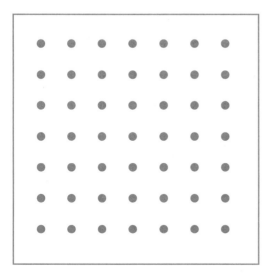

6.

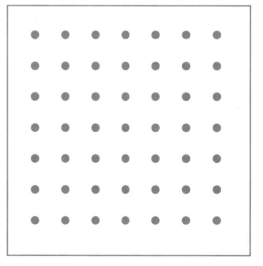

LESSON 10·7 **Math Boxes**

---

1. Draw at least one line of symmetry.

MRB
60

2. Color $\frac{2}{3}$ of the leaves green.

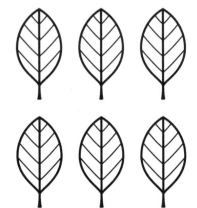

---

3. Write as dollars and cents. Eight dollars and forty-three cents:

_____

fifteen dollars and 6 cents:

_____

fifty dollars and seventeen

cents: _____

4.

in	out
32	
56	
45	
	97
89	

Rule
+9

MRB
101 102

---

5. Write <, >, or =.

1 hour _____ 30 minutes

3 months _____ 1 year

7 days _____ 1 week

6. Use counters to solve.
15 marbles are shared equally. Each child gets 6 marbles. How many children are sharing?

_____ children

How many marbles are left over?

_____ marbles

---

1) MR 1.2   2) NS 4.2   3) NS 5.2
4) AF 1.3   5) MG 1.4   6) NS 3.2

Money Exchange Game Directions

LESSON 10·8

Materials
- ☐ 1 six-sided die
- ☐ 1 ten- or twelve-sided die
- ☐ 24 pennies, 39 dimes, thirty-nine $1 bills, and one $10 bill per player

Players   2 or 3

Skill   Make exchanges between coins and bills

Object of the Game   To be the first to trade for $10

Directions

1. Each player puts 12 pennies, 12 dimes, twelve $1 bills, and one $10 bill in the bank.

2. Players take turns. Players use a six-sided die to represent pennies. Players use a ten- or twelve-sided die to represent dimes.

3. Each player

   ◆ rolls the dice.

   ◆ takes from the bank the number of pennies and dimes shown on the faces of the dice.

   ◆ puts the coins in the correct columns on his or her Place-Value Mat on journal page 254.

4. Whenever possible, a player replaces 10 coins or bills of a lower denomination with a coin or bill of the next higher denomination.

5. The first player to trade for a $10 bill wins.

If there is a time limit, the winner is the player with the largest number on the mat when time is up.

LESSON 10·8   Place-Value Mat

pennies (P)			
1s			

dimes (D)			
10s			

$1 dollars			
100s			

$10			
1,000s			

Number Sense 1.1, 1.2, 5.0

LESSON 10·8 Ballpark Estimates

Fill in the unit box. Then, for each problem:

Make a ballpark estimate before you add.

Write a number model for your estimate.

Use your calculator and solve the problem. Write the exact answer in the box.

Compare your estimate to your answer.

Unit

1. Ballpark estimate:	2. Ballpark estimate:	3. Ballpark estimate:
_____	_____	_____
148 + 27	163 + 32	133 + 35
4. Ballpark estimate:	5. Ballpark estimate:	6. Ballpark estimate:
_____	_____	_____
143 + 41	184 + 23	154 + 83

LESSON 10·8   **Math Boxes**

---

1. What number is shown by the blocks?

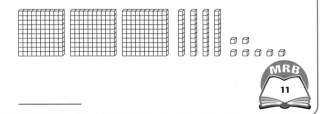

MRB
11

_____

---

2. Kelly has $10. Her lunch total was $8.75. How much change will she get?

_____

---

3. In the morning, it was 62°F. By afternoon, the temperature was 75°F. How much did the temperature rise? _____

Change

| Start | → | End |

_____

Number model: _____

MRB
116–118

---

4. Cross out the names that don't belong.

10¢

ten cents, $\frac{1}{10}$ of a dollar,

$10.00, ⒟, ⓃⓃ, $0.01,

$\frac{1}{100}$ of a dollar,

$\frac{1}{2}$ of a dollar

MRB
88–90

---

5. Which object is shaped like a cone? Circle the best answer.

A   shoe box

B   party hat

C   paper towel roll

D   globe

MRB
57

---

6. 4 ladybugs. 5 spots on each ladybug. How many spots?

_____

Fill in the diagram and write a number model.

lady bugs	spots per lady bug	spots in all

_____ × _____ = _____

MRB
112 113

---

 1) NS 1.2   2) NS 5.0   3) AF 1.0
4) NS 5.0   5) MG **2.0**   6) NS **3.1**

LESSON 10·9 **Math Boxes**

---

1. Use your Pattern-Block Template.

Trace a trapezoid. Draw the line of symmetry.

MRB
54 55
60

2. Color $\frac{3}{4}$ of the circle.

What fraction of the circle is not colored? _____

---

3. Write the amounts.

Five thousand six hundred eight dollars and twelve cents

_____

Two hundred sixteen dollars and sixty-eight cents

_____

Three hundred nine dollars and five cents

_____

4.

Rule	in	out
12 in. = 1ft	6	
		2
	48	

MRB
101 102

---

5. _____ hours in a day

_____ days in a week

_____ months in a year

_____ weeks in a year

6. Use counters to solve. 26 children. 2 children for each computer. How many computers?

_____ computers

MRB
114 115

LESSON 10·10 **Place Value**

1. Match names.

   A. 5 ones   _____ 50

   B. 5 tens   _____ 500

   C. 5 hundreds   _____ 50,000

   D. 5 thousands   _____ 5

   E. 5 ten-thousands   _____ 5,000

Fill in the blanks. Write ones, tens, hundreds, thousands, or ten-thousands.

2. The 7 in 187 stands for 7 _____.

3. The 2 in 2,785 stands for 2 _____.

4. The 3 in 4,239 stands for 3 _____.

5. The 0 in 13,409 stands for 0 _____.

6. The 5 in 58,047 stands for 5 _____.

Continue.

7. 364; 365; 366; _____; _____; _____

8. 996; 997; 998; _____; _____; _____

9. 1,796; 1,797; 1,798; _____; _____; _____

10. 1,996; 1,997; 1,998; _____; _____; _____

11. 9,996; 9,997; 9,998; _____; _____; _____

Number Sense 1.0, **1.1**, 1.2

LESSON 10·10 **Math Boxes**

---

1. Circle the digit in the 1,000s place.

4, 6 9 4

2 9, 4 0 0

2 0, 0 0 4

5, 0 1 9

Read each number to a partner.

MRB 10

2. I have a 5-dollar bill. I spend $4.38. How much change do I get?

_____

3. Show 25°C on the thermometer.

Is it good weather to go ice skating or to go to the beach?

_____

4. Write 5 names for $0.75.

_____

_____

_____

_____

_____

5. Write the names of 3 objects shaped like rectangular prisms.

_____

_____

_____

MRB 56

6. 5 wagons. 4 wheels on each wagon. How many wheels?

_____ wheels

wagons	wheels per wagon	wheels in all

MRB 112 113

LESSON 10·11 Parentheses Puzzles

Parentheses can make a big difference in a problem.

Example:

$15 - 5 + 3 = ?$

$(15 - 5) + 3 = (10) + 3 = 13$; but

$15 - (5 + 3) = 15 - (8) = 7$

Solve problems containing parentheses.

1. $7 + (8 - 3) =$ _____

2. $(4 + 11) - 6 =$ _____

3. $8 + (13 - 9) =$ _____

4. _____ $= (12 + 8) - 16$

5. $140 - (20 + 80) =$ _____

6. _____ $= (30 + 40) - 70$

Put in parentheses to solve the puzzles.

7. $12 - 4 + 6 = 14$

8. $15 - 9 - 4 = 10$

9. $140 - 60 + 30 = 110$

10. $500 = 400 - 100 + 200$

11. $3 \times 2 + 5 = 11$

12. $2 \times 5 - 5 = 0$

Number Sense **2.2**, **3.0**; Algebra and Functions **1.1**

LESSON
10·11   **Math Boxes**

---

1. Choose any shape on your Pattern-Block Template that has at least 2 lines of symmetry. Trace the shape and draw the lines of symmetry.

2. Circle $\frac{3}{12}$.

   • • • •
   • • • •
   • • • •

   What fraction of dots is not circled? Circle the best answer.

   A $\frac{9}{3}$ **B** $\frac{9}{12}$

   C $\frac{6}{12}$ **D** $\frac{3}{9}$

   Write another name for this fraction _____.

---

3. Use your calculator to find the total.

   $\boxed{\$1}$ $\boxed{\$1}$ $\boxed{\$1}$ $\boxed{\$1}$ = $ _____

   Ⓠ Ⓠ Ⓠ = $ _____

   Ⓓ Ⓓ Ⓓ Ⓓ Ⓓ = $ _____

   Ⓝ Ⓝ Ⓝ Ⓝ Ⓝ Ⓝ Ⓝ = $ _____

   Total = $ _____

4.
Rule	Ⓝ	Ⓠ
$5Ⓝ = 1Ⓠ$		3
		4
	30	
		10
		20

---

5. _____ months = 1 year

   _____ months = 2 years

   _____ months = 3 years

   _____ months = 4 years

6. You have 18 pieces of gum to share equally. If each child gets 4 pieces, how many children are sharing?

   _____ children

   How many pieces of gum are left over?

   _____ pieces of gum

LESSON 10·12   Math Boxes

1. 6 lily pads. 3 frogs per lily pad. How many frogs in all?

_____ frogs

Fill in the diagram and write a number model.

lily pads	frogs per lily pad	frogs in all

_____ × _____ = _____

2. Draw a 7-by-3 array.

How many in all? _____

3. 17 magazines are shared equally among 5 children. Draw a picture to help you.

Each child gets ___ magazines.

There are ___ magazines left.

4. 8 books per shelf. 4 shelves. Fill in the diagram and solve.

shelves	books per shelf	books in all

There are _____ books.

5. This is a _____ -by- _____ array.

How many dots in all?

_____ dots

• • • • •
• • • • •
• • • • •
• • • • •
• • • • •

6. 11 balloons are shared equally among 4 children. How many balloons does each child get?

_____ balloons

How many are left over?

_____ balloons

1) NS 3.1   2) NS 3.1   3) NS 3.2
4) NS 3.1   5) NS 3.1   6) NS 3.2

LESSON 11·1 **Math Boxes**

---

1. Circle the unit that makes sense.

Grandma's house is

5 _____ away.   km   dm

Mona's goldfish is

8 _____ long.   cm   m

Ahmed's dad is

68 _____ tall.   cm   in.

---

2. Circle the fraction that is bigger.
Use your Fraction Cards to help.

$\frac{2}{3}$ or $\frac{2}{2}$ $\frac{4}{5}$ or $\frac{2}{5}$

$\frac{2}{8}$ or $\frac{5}{6}$ $\frac{3}{6}$ or $\frac{1}{4}$

---

3. Write a number with 5 in the thousands place.

_____

What is the value of the digit 5 in your number?

_____

---

4. Draw a 3-by-6 array.

How many in all? _____

---

5. Had a $10 bill.
Spent $8.90.
How much change?

_____

---

6. Write the fact family.

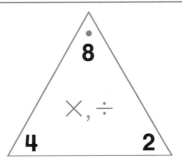

_____ ✕ _____ = _____

_____ ✕ _____ = _____

_____ ÷ _____ = _____

_____ ÷ _____ = _____

LESSON 11·1   Art Supply Poster

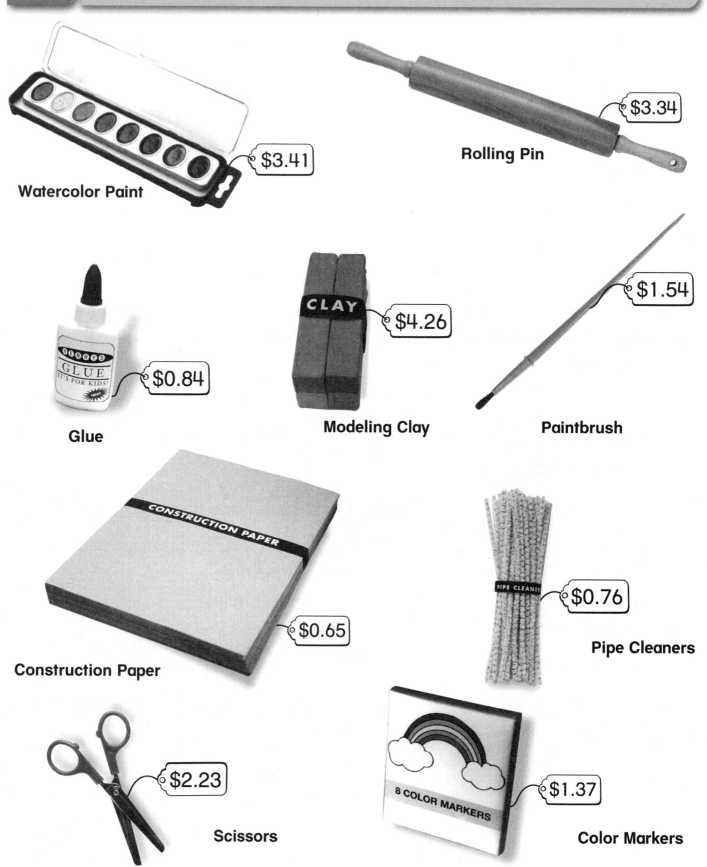

$3.41 — Watercolor Paint

$3.34 — Rolling Pin

$0.84 — Glue

$4.26 — Modeling Clay

$1.54 — Paintbrush

$0.65 — Construction Paper

$0.76 — Pipe Cleaners

$2.23 — Scissors

$1.37 — Color Markers

NS 2.0, 5.1, 5.2, 6.0; MR 2.1

LESSON 11·1 Buying Art Supplies

Estimate the total cost for each pair of items.

Write your estimate in the answer space.

Add to find the total cost.

Check your estimate with your total cost.

1. pipe cleaners and watercolors	2. clay and construction paper	3. paintbrush and scissors
Estimated Cost **Total Cost**	**Estimated Cost** **Total Cost**	**Estimated Cost** **Total Cost**
4. glue and construction paper	5. markers and glue	6. clay and rolling pin
Estimated Cost **Total Cost**	**Estimated Cost** **Total Cost**	**Estimated Cost** **Total Cost**

LESSON 11·2 **Comparing Costs**

Use the Art Supply Poster on journal page 264.
In Problems 1–6, circle the item that costs more.
Then find how much more.

1. glue or markers How much more? _____	**2.** construction paper or paintbrush How much more? _____
3. pipe cleaners or paintbrush How much more? _____	**4.** rolling pin or scissors How much more? _____
5. watercolors or markers How much more? _____	**6.** paintbrush or watercolors How much more? _____

7. You buy a pack of construction paper. You pay with a $1 bill.

Should you get more or less than 2 quarters in change? _____

8. You buy pipe cleaners. You pay with a $1 bill.

How much change should you get? _____

9. You buy a rolling pin. You pay with a $5 bill.

How much change should you get? _____

NS 2.0, 5.0, 5.1, 5.2; MR 2.0, 2.2

LESSON 11·2   Data Analysis

Lily collected information about the ages of people in her family.

Complete.

Name	Age
Dave	40
Dedra	36
Jamal	12
Tyler	10
Lily	8

1. The oldest person is _____.

   Age: _____ years

2. The youngest person is _____.

   Age: _____ years

3. Range of the ages (oldest minus the youngest):

   _____ years

4. Middle value of the ages: _____ years

Fill in the blanks with the name of the correct person.

5. Jamal is about 4 years older than _____.

6. Tyler is about 26 years younger than _____.

7. Dedra is about 3 times as old as _____.

8. Dave is about 4 times as old as _____.

Try This

9. Tyler is about $\frac{1}{4}$ as old as _____.

LESSON 11·2   **Math Boxes**

---

1. Solve and show your work.

$$47 \atop {-\ 39}$$

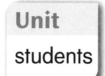

Unit

students

---

2. What is the minimum number (the smallest) in the list?

_____

2,371; 429; 578; 1,261

MRB
45

---

3. What shape is a globe? Circle the best answer.

A. sphere

B. rectangular prism

C. cone

D. cylinder

MRB
56–59

---

4. 20 campers divided equally among 5 tents. How many campers in each tent?

_____ campers

---

5. Fill in the missing numbers.

	1,065
1,074	

---

6. What is the range of this set of numbers (the largest minus the smallest)?

_____

75, 93, 108, 52

MRB
45

---

1) NS 2.2   2) SDAP 1.3   3) MG 2.0
4) NS 3.2   5) SDAP 2.1   6) SDAP 1.3

LESSON 11·3 Trade-First Subtraction

◆ Make a ballpark estimate for each problem and write a number model for your ballpark estimate.

◆ Use the trade-first method of subtraction to solve each problem.

Example:

Ballpark estimate:

$$40 - 20 = 20$$

longs 10s	cubes 1s
2	17
~~3~~	~~7~~
− 1	9
1	8

Answer
18

---

1. Ballpark estimate:

_____

longs 10s	cubes 1s
2	8
− 1	9

Answer

---

2. Ballpark estimate:

_____

longs 10s	cubes 1s
3	1
− 1	7

Answer

---

3. Ballpark estimate:

_____

longs 10s	cubes 1s
7	6
− 5	9

Answer

---

4. Ballpark estimate:

_____

longs 10s	cubes 1s
3	5
− 2	6

Answer

---

5. Ballpark estimate:

_____

longs 10s	cubes 1s
4	4
− 2	7

Answer

LESSON 11·3   **Math Boxes**

---

1. The perimeter is about

_____ cm.

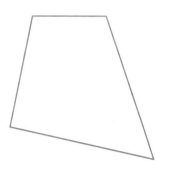

---

2. Divide into:

halves   fourths

Write <, >, or =.

$\frac{1}{2}$ _____ $\frac{1}{4}$ $\frac{2}{4}$ _____ $\frac{1}{2}$

$\frac{1}{2}$ _____ $\frac{3}{4}$

---

3. What is the value of the digit 4 in each number?

14 _____

142 _____

436 _____

4,678 _____

4.

_____-by-_____ array

How many in all? _____

---

5. I had a 10-dollar bill. I spent $5.23. How much change did I receive? Fill in the circle next to the best answer.

Ⓐ $3.80   Ⓑ $4.77

Ⓒ $5.00   Ⓓ $15.23

---

6. Complete the Fact Triangle. Write the fact family.

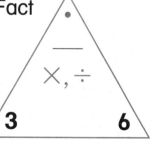

_____ × _____ = _____

_____ × _____ = _____

_____ ÷ _____ = _____

_____ ÷ _____ = _____

---

1) MG 1.0   2) NS 4.1   3) NS 1.1
4) NS 3.1   5) NS 5.1   6) NS 3.0

LESSON 11·4 **Math Boxes**

---

1. Solve and show your work.

$$71 - 23$$

Unit

---

2. What is the maximum number (the largest) in the list?

_____

7,946; 2,599; 17,949; 8,112

MRB 45

---

3. What shape is a can of soup?

_____

MRB 56–59

---

4. 15 baseball cards are shared equally among 4 children. How many cards does each child get?

____ cards

How many left over? _____

---

5. Fill in the missing numbers.

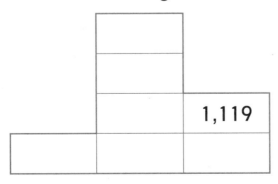

1,119

---

6. What is the range of this list of numbers (the largest minus the smallest)?

_____

29, 132, 56, 30

MRB 45

LESSON 11·4 Multiplication Number Stories

1. 4 insects on the flower. How many legs in all?

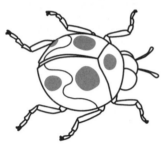

Has 6 legs

insects	legs per insect	legs in all

Answer: _____ legs

Number model: _____ × _____ = _____

2. 3 vans full of people. How many people in all?

Holds 10 people

vans	people per van	people in all

Answer: _____ people

Number model: _____ × _____ = _____

3. 9 windows. How many panes in all?

Has 4 panes

windows	panes per window	panes in all

Answer: _____ panes

Number model: _____ × _____ = _____

Number Sense **3.0**, **3.1**; Mathematical Reasoning 1.2

Date _____   Time _____

Try This

Use the pictures to make up two multiplication number stories.

Has 7 candles

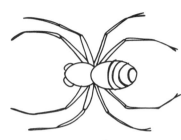

Has 8 legs

Has 5 players

For each story:

◆ Fill in the multiplication diagram.

◆ Draw a picture or array and find the answer.

◆ Fill in the number model.

4. _____

_____

_____

_____	_____	_____
	per _____	in all

Answer: _____

Number model: _____ × _____ = _____

5. _____

_____

_____

_____	_____	_____
	per _____	in all

Answer: _____

Number model: _____ × _____ = _____

LESSON 11·5 Division Number Stories

For each number story:

◆ Fill in the diagram.

◆ On a separate sheet of paper, draw a picture or array and find the answer. Complete the sentences.

◆ Fill in the number model.

1. Five children are playing a game with a deck of 30 cards. How many cards can the dealer give each player?

children	cards per child	cards in all

_____ cards to each player.   _____ cards are left over.

Number model: _____ ÷ _____ → _____ R_____

2. The pet shop has 12 puppies in pens. There are 4 puppies in each pen. How many pens have puppies in them?

pens	puppies per pen	puppies in all

_____ pens have puppies in them.   _____ puppies are left over.

Number model: _____ ÷ _____ → _____ R_____

3. Tennis balls are sold 3 to a can. Luis buys 15 balls. How many cans is that?

cans	balls per can	balls in all

Luis buys _____ cans.

Number model: _____ ÷ _____ → _____ R_____

Number Sense 3.0, 3.2; **Mathematical Reasoning 1.2**

LESSON 11·5   **Division Number Stories** *continued*

4. Eight children share 18 toys equally. How many toys does each child get?

_____	_____	_____
	per _____	**in all**

Each child gets _____ toys.

_____ toys are left over.

Number model: _____ ÷ _____ → _____ R _____

---

5. Seven friends share 24 marbles equally. How many marbles does each friend get?

_____	_____	_____
	per _____	**in all**

Each friend gets _____ marbles.   _____ marbles are left over.

Number model: _____ ÷ _____ → _____ R _____

Try This

6. Tina is storing 20 packages of seeds in boxes. Each box holds 6 packages. How many boxes does Tina need to store all the packages? (Be careful. Think!)

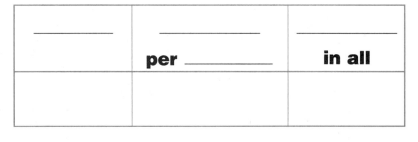

_____	_____	_____
	per _____	**in all**

Tina needs _____ boxes.

Number model: _____ ÷ _____ → _____ R _____

LESSON 11·5   **Math Boxes**

---

1. 8 flower boxes. 4 plants in each box. How many plants?

_____ plants

Fill in the diagram and write a number model.

boxes	plants per box	plants in all

_____ × _____ = _____

MRB 112 113

2.

• • • •
• • • •

_____-by-_____ array

How many dots in all? _____

---

3. Use the partial-sums algorithm to solve. Show your work. Circle the best answer.

$$\begin{array}{r} 78 \\ + 26 \\ \hline \end{array}$$

A. 92   **B.** 52

C. 94   **D.** 104

MRB 30

---

4. Count by ones.

5,099; _____; _____;

5,102; _____; _____;

5,105; _____; _____

---

5. Use an inch ruler to find the perimeter of the hexagon.

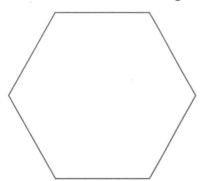

The perimeter is _____ inches.

MRB 68

---

6. Complete the table.

Rule ×2

in	out
0	
1	
2	
	6
4	
	10

MRB 100–102

---

1) NS 3.1   2) NS 3.1   3) NS 2.2
4) SDAP 2.2 5) MG 1.0   6) AF 1.3

LESSON 11·6   Multiplication Facts List

I am listing the times _____ facts.

If you are not sure of a fact, draw an array with Os or Xs.

2 × _____ = _____

3 × _____ = _____

4 × _____ = _____

5 × _____ = _____

6 × _____ = _____

7 × _____ = _____

8 × _____ = _____

9 × _____ = _____

10 × _____ = _____

LESSON 11·6 Using Arrays to Find Products

Draw an array to help you find each product.
Use Xs to draw your arrays.

1. $2 \times 4 =$ _____

X X X X
X X X X

2. $4 \times 2 =$ _____

3. $6 \times 5 =$ _____

4. $5 \times 6 =$ _____

5. $5 \times 5 =$ _____

6. $2 \times 10 =$ _____

Try This

7. $4 \times 15 =$ _____

Number Sense **3.0**, **3.1**, **3.3**

---

1. Subtract. Show your work.

$$\begin{array}{r} 72 \\ -\ 35 \\ \hline \end{array}$$

Unit

2. What is the median (the middle value) for this list of numbers?

_____

51, 82, 51, 23, 23, 67

MRB 46

---

3. This line segment is

_____ cm long.

_____

Draw a line segment 4 cm longer.

4. I have a pile of 16 counters.

$\dfrac{1}{2} =$ _____ counters

$\dfrac{8}{16} =$ _____ counters

---

5. Find the rules.

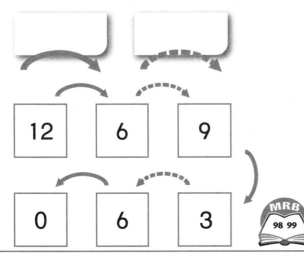

6. Write the mode for this set of numbers (the number that occurs the most often).

_____

29, 17, 39, 12, 17

MRB 45

LESSON 11·7 Products Table

0×0 = **0**	0×1 =	0×2 =	0×3 =	0×4 =	0×5 =	0×6 =	0×7 =	0×8 =	0×9 =	0×10 =
1×0 =	1×1 = **1**	1×2 =	1×3 =	1×4 =	1×5 =	1×6 =	1×7 =	1×8 =	1×9 =	1×10 =
2×0 =	2×1 =	2×2 = **4**	2×3 =	2×4 =	2×5 =	2×6 =	2×7 =	2×8 =	2×9 =	2×10 =
3×0 =	3×1 =	3×2 =	3×3 = **9**	3×4 =	3×5 =	3×6 =	3×7 =	3×8 =	3×9 =	3×10 =
4×0 =	4×1 =	4×2 =	4×3 =	4×4 = **16**	4×5 =	4×6 =	4×7 =	4×8 =	4×9 =	4×10 =
5×0 =	5×1 =	5×2 =	5×3 =	5×4 =	5×5 = **25**	5×6 =	5×7 =	5×8 =	5×9 =	5×10 =
6×0 =	6×1 =	6×2 =	6×3 =	6×4 =	6×5 =	6×6 = **36**	6×7 =	6×8 =	6×9 =	6×10 =
7×0 =	7×1 =	7×2 =	7×3 =	7×4 =	7×5 =	7×6 =	7×7 = **49**	7×8 =	7×9 =	7×10 =
8×0 =	8×1 =	8×2 =	8×3 =	8×4 =	8×5 =	8×6 =	8×7 =	8×8 = **64**	8×9 =	8×10 =
9×0 =	9×1 =	9×2 =	9×3 =	9×4 =	9×5 =	9×6 =	9×7 =	9×8 =	9×9 = **81**	9×10 =
10×0 =	10×1 =	10×2 =	10×3 =	10×4 =	10×5 =	10×6 =	10×7 =	10×8 =	10×9 =	10×10 = **100**

Number Sense **3.0**, **3.1**, **3.3**; Algebra and Functions **1.1**

LESSON
11·7   **Math Boxes**

---

1. 5 nests with 3 eggs in each. How many eggs in all?

_____ eggs

nests	eggs per nest	eggs in all

_____ × _____ = _____

112 113

---

2. Maria has 9 pairs of shoes in her closet. How many shoes does she have in all?

Draw an array.

_____ × _____ = _____

_____ shoes

---

3. Solve.

Unit
baby alligators

_____ = 24 + 41

33 + 12 = _____

_____ = 52 + 15

16 + 51 = _____

---

4. Count by thousands. Fill in the circle next to the best answer.

2,324; _____; 4,324

Ⓐ 3,224   Ⓑ 2,424

Ⓒ 3,324   Ⓓ 3,434

---

5. Draw a rectangle.
Make two sides
3 inches long.
Make the other two sides
2 inches long.

---

6. Complete the table.

Rule
×2

in	out
20	
	60
40	

100–102

LESSON 11·8   **Multiplication/Division Fact Families**

Write the fact family for each Fact Triangle.

1.
```
      10
     ×, ÷
   2      5
```
$\underline{5} \times \underline{2} = \underline{10}$

$\underline{} \times \underline{} = \underline{}$

$\underline{10} \div \underline{2} = \underline{5}$

$\underline{} \div \underline{} = \underline{}$

2.
```
      12
     ×, ÷
   3      4
```
$\underline{} \times \underline{} = \underline{}$

$\underline{} \times \underline{} = \underline{}$

$\underline{} \div \underline{} = \underline{}$

$\underline{} \div \underline{} = \underline{}$

3.
```
      21
     ×, ÷
   3      7
```
$\underline{} \times \underline{} = \underline{}$

$\underline{} \times \underline{} = \underline{}$

$\underline{} \div \underline{} = \underline{}$

$\underline{} \div \underline{} = \underline{}$

4.
```
      40
     ×, ÷
   5      8
```
$\underline{} \times \underline{} = \underline{}$

$\underline{} \times \underline{} = \underline{}$

$\underline{} \div \underline{} = \underline{}$

$\underline{} \div \underline{} = \underline{}$

5.
```
      54
     ×, ÷
   6      9
```
$\underline{} \times \underline{} = \underline{}$

$\underline{} \times \underline{} = \underline{}$

$\underline{} \div \underline{} = \underline{}$

$\underline{} \div \underline{} = \underline{}$

6.
```
      28
     ×, ÷
   4      7
```
$\underline{} \times \underline{} = \underline{}$

$\underline{} \times \underline{} = \underline{}$

$\underline{} \div \underline{} = \underline{}$

$\underline{} \div \underline{} = \underline{}$

LESSON 11·8   Multiplication and Division with 2, 5, and 10

1. double 8 = _____   _____ = double 9

   2 × 4 = _____   _____ = 2 × 1

   7 × 2 = _____   _____ = 0 × 2

2. 40 cents = _____ nickels   5 ÷ 1 = _____

   15 ÷ 5 = _____   _____ nickels = 25 cents

3. 40 cents = _____ dimes   _____ ÷ 10 = 6

   20 ÷ 10 = _____   _____ dimes = 90 cents

4. For each multiplication fact, give two division facts in the same fact family.

   2 × 6 = 12 $\underline{12} \div \underline{2} = \underline{6}$ $\underline{12} \div \underline{6} = \underline{2}$

   5 × 9 = 45   _____ ÷ _____ = _____   _____ ÷ _____ = _____

   10 × 4 = 40   _____ ÷ _____ = _____   _____ ÷ _____ = _____

   3 × 2 = 6   _____ ÷ _____ = _____   _____ ÷ _____ = _____

   8 × 5 = 40   _____ ÷ _____ = _____   _____ ÷ _____ = _____

   5 × 10 = 50   _____ ÷ _____ = _____   _____ ÷ _____ = _____

LESSON 11·8   **Math Boxes**

---

1. Subtract. Show your work.

$$90 - 64$$ $$37 - 18$$

Unit

2. What is the median (the middle value) for this list of numbers?

_____

50, 31, 41, 42, 41

---

3. Draw a line segment 3 cm long.

Draw a second line segment 4 cm longer than the first.

Draw a third line segment twice as long as the first.

4. Get 21 counters.

$\frac{1}{3}$ = _____ counters

$\frac{2}{7}$ = _____ counters

$\frac{3}{3}$ = _____ counters

---

5. Complete the frames.

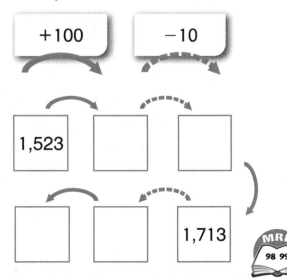

6. Find the mode (the number that occurs most often). Choose the best answer.

496, 738, 713, 100, 713

⚬ 713   ⚬ 496

⚬ 100   ⚬ 738

MRB 45

1) NS 2.2   2) SDAP 1.3   3) MG 1.3
4) NS 4.2   5) SDAP 2.2   6) SDAP 1.3

1. Each ladybug has 5 spots. 20 spots in all.

How many ladybugs? _____

Fill in the diagram and write a number model.

ladybugs	spots per ladybug	spots in all

_____ × _____ = _____

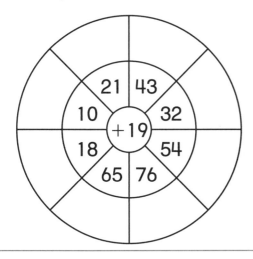

2. Multiply. If you need help, make arrays.

Unit

$4 \times 5 =$ _____

$6 \times 2 =$ _____

$1 \times 10 =$ _____

3. Complete.

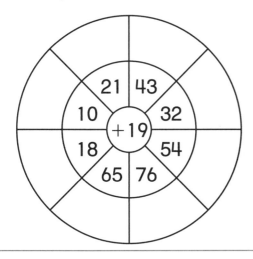

```
        21 | 43
    10  +19  32
        18  54
        65 | 76
```

4. Write the number that is 1,000 more than:

7,542 _____

1,837 _____

5,641 _____

8,863 _____

5. Draw a line 1 inch long.

Draw another line twice as long.

6. Find the rule. Complete the table.

in	out
10¢	20¢
15¢	30¢
	50¢
60¢	

Rule

LESSON 11·9 *Beat the Calculator*

Materials   ☐ calculator

Players   3 (Caller, Brain, and Calculator)

Directions

1. The Caller reads fact problems from the Brain's journal—in the order listed on the next page.

2. The Brain solves each problem and says the answer.

3. While the Brain is working on the answer, the Calculator solves each problem using a calculator and says the answer.

4. If the Brain beats the Calculator, the Caller makes a check mark next to the fact in the Brain's journal.

LESSON 11·9 *Beat the Calculator* continued

✓	✓	✓	Fact Problem
			2 × 4 = _____
			3 × 5 = _____
			2 × 2 = _____
			4 × 3 = _____
			5 × 5 = _____
			6 × 2 = _____
			6 × 5 = _____
			3 × 3 = _____
			4 × 5 = _____
			3 × 6 = _____

✓	✓	✓	Fact Problem
			7 × 3 = _____
			5 × 2 = _____
			6 × 4 = _____
			2 × 7 = _____
			3 × 2 = _____
			4 × 4 = _____
			4 × 1 = _____
			4 × 7 = _____
			7 × 5 = _____
			0 × 2 = _____

1. What is the range of this set of numbers (the largest number minus the smallest number)?

_____

81, 910, 109, 175

MRB
45

2. Find the mode (the number that occurs most often).

_____

183, 56, 618, 56, 215, 56, 183, 56

MRB
45

3. Complete the Fact Triangle. Write the fact family.

×, ÷
5   9

_____ × _____ = _____

_____ × _____ = _____

_____ ÷ _____ = _____

_____ ÷ _____ = _____

MRB
38

4. Find the median (the middle number).

_____

640, 710, 615, 915, 320

MRB
46

5. Complete the table.

Rule ×2	in	out
	100	
		400
	1,000	
		4,000

MRB
100–102

6. Complete the Fact Triangle. Write the fact family.

27
×, ÷
3   ____

_____ × _____ = _____

_____ × _____ = _____

_____ ÷ _____ = _____

_____ ÷ _____ = _____

MRB
38

1) SDAP 1.3   2) SDAP 1.3   3) NS 3.0
4) SDAP 1.3   5) AF 1.3   6) NS 3.0

LESSON 12·1   **Review: Telling Time**

1. How many hours do clock faces show? _____ hours

2. How long does it take the hour hand to move from one number to the next? _____

3. How long does it take the minute hand to move from one number to the next? _____

4. How many times does the hour hand move around the clock face in one day? _____ times

5. How many times does the minute hand move around the clock face in one day? _____ times

Write the time shown by each clock.

6.

_____ : _____

7.

_____ : _____

8.

_____ : _____

Draw the hour and minute hands to match the time.

9.

8:00

10.

6:45

11.

4:10

LESSON 12·1 **Math Boxes**

---

1. Jordan spent $6.38 on a book and $1.23 on a magazine. How much did he spend all together? First estimate the costs and the total.

_____ + _____ = _____

Then solve.

2. 1 hour = _____ minutes

$\frac{1}{2}$ hour = _____ minutes

$\frac{1}{4}$ hour = _____ minutes

$\frac{3}{4}$ hour = _____ minutes

$1\frac{1}{2}$ hours = _____ minutes

---

3. Write a fraction for each shaded part. Put <, >, or = in the box.

4. I spent $4.22 at the store and gave the cashier a $10 bill. How much change should I get?

$_____

5.

5,401	1,290	632
3,679	890	798

The minimum number is

_____ .

The maximum number is

_____ .

6. A pentagon has ___ sides.

A hexagon has ___ sides.

An octagon has ___ sides.

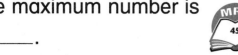

1) NS 2.0   2) MG 1.4   3) NS 4.1
4) NS 5.1   5) SDAP 1.3   6) MG 2.1

LESSON 12·2 Time Before and After

1. It is:

Show the time
20 minutes later.

What time is it?

_____ : _____

2. It is:

Show the time
35 minutes later.

What time is it?

_____ : _____

3. It is:

Show the time
15 minutes earlier.

What time is it?

_____ : _____

4. You pick a time. Draw
the hands on the clock.

It is:

Show the time
50 minutes later.

What time is it?

_____ : _____

LESSON 12·2 **Many Names for Times**

What time does each clock show? Fill in the ovals next to the correct names.

Example: ● quarter-past 1   ● 15 minutes after 1

O two ten   O 5 minutes after 3

● one fifteen

---

1. O seven fifteen   O quarter-to 7

O quarter-to 8   O quarter-past 8

O quarter-past 7

---

2. O half-past 10   O eleven thirty

O half-past 11   O 30 minutes after 10

O ten thirty

---

3. O quarter-past 5   O quarter-to 6

O quarter-to 5   O six fifteen

O five forty-five

---

4. O nine forty   O 20 to 8

O 20 to 9   O eight forty

O 40 minutes to 9

Measurement and Geometry 1.4

LESSON 12·2 Addition and Subtraction Strategies

Add or subtract. Use your favorite addition or subtraction strategy.

1. 53 + 45	**2.** 36 + 48	**3.** 456 + 17
Answer	Answer	Answer
4. 68 − 24	**5.** 65 − 27	**6.** 516 − 38
Answer	Answer	Answer

LESSON 12·2 **Math Boxes**

1.

Favorite Animals of Ms. Lee's Classroom

Whales	✕✕✕
Manatees	✕✕✕✕✕✕
Walruses	✕✕✕✕✕
Cubs	✕✕✕✕✕✕✕✕✕

Which animal was the most

popular? _____

---

2. Solve.

Unit
[   ]

$(14 - 7) + 4 =$ _____

$14 - (7 + 4) =$ _____

$(12 - 7) + 5 =$ _____

$12 - (7 + 5) =$ _____

---

3. Write < or >.

2,469 _____ 12,469

60,278 _____ 50,278

25,100 _____ 25,110

MRB
9

---

4. What item is the shape of a rectangular prism? Circle the best answer.

A doughnut

B can of soup

C book

D traffic cone

MRB
56

5.

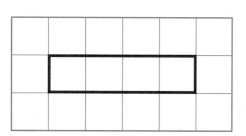

The area is _____ sq cm.

The perimeter is _____ cm.

MRB
68 69

---

6. The pet store sold 12 fish. $\frac{1}{2}$ were guppies and $\frac{1}{4}$ were neons. The rest were angelfish. How many of each?

There were _____ guppies.

There were _____ neons.

There were _____ angelfish.

---

1) SDAP 1.4   2) AF 1.1   3) NS 1.3
4) MG 2.0   5) MG 1.0   6) NS 4.2

LESSON 12·3 Important Events in Communication

For each event below, make a dot on the timeline
and write the letter for the event above the dot.

A telephone (1876)

B radio (1906)

C television (1926)

D telegraph (1837)

E CD player (1982)

F copier (1937)

G audiocassette (1963)

H phonograph (1877)

I personal computer (1974)

J movie machine (1894)

K 3-D movies (1922)

L videocassette (1969)

M typewriter (1867)

N FM radio (1933)

A •

LESSON 12·3 Math Boxes

1. A baseball costs $3.69. A yo-yo costs $1.49. You buy both.

Estimate the cost:

_____ + _____ = _____

Actual cost:

$_____

2. Naquon grew 2 inches in _____.
Circle the best answer.

  A 1 day

  B 5 minutes

  C 1 year

  D 24 hours

3. Write four names for $\frac{1}{2}$. Use your Fraction Cards to help.

_____, _____, _____, _____

Write 2 fractions that are:

greater than $\frac{1}{2}$. _____, _____

less than $\frac{1}{2}$. _____, _____

4. I bought a beach ball for $1.49 and a sand toy for $3.96. How much change will I get from a $10 bill?

$_____

5. $24.06 $9.99 $14.98
$19.99 $29.83

The maximum is

$_____.

The minimum is

$_____.

6. Draw two polygons with 4 sides.

MRB 45

MRB 52

1) NS 2.0   2) NS 6.1   3) NS 4.1
4) NS 5.1   5) SDAP 1.3   6) MG 2.1

LESSON 12·4 Subtraction Practice

Fill in the unit box. Then, for each problem:

◆ Make a ballpark estimate before you subtract.

◆ Write a number model for your estimate. Then solve the problem. For Problems 1 and 2, use the trade-first algorithm. For Problems 3–6, use any strategy you choose.

◆ Compare your estimate to your answer.

Unit
_____

1. Ballpark estimate: _____ $25 - 18 =$ _____	**2.** Ballpark estimate: _____ $31 - 22 =$ _____	**3.** Ballpark estimate: _____ $53 - 29 =$ _____
4. Ballpark estimate: _____ $87 - 39 =$ _____	**5.** Ballpark estimate: _____ $148 - 29 =$ _____	**6.** Ballpark estimate: _____ $177 - 48 =$ _____

LESSON 12·4 **Math Boxes**

1.

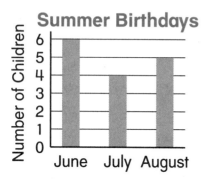

Summer Birthdays

How many birthdays are in June and July? _____

2. Add parentheses to make the number models true.

Unit
children

$18 - 13 - 4 = 9$

$18 - 13 - 4 = 1$

$27 - 6 + 10 = 31$

$4 \times 2 + 3 = 20$

---

3. Write <, >, or =.

$10{,}000$ _____ $9{,}999$

$33{,}231$ _____ $30{,}231$

$75{,}679$ _____ $75{,}855$

MRB
9

4. Name 3 objects that are shaped like a cone.

_____

_____

_____

MRB
57

---

5. Solve.

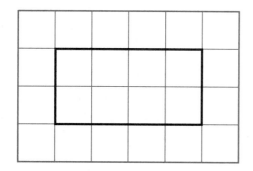

Area: _____ sq cm

Perimeter: _____ cm

MRB
68 69

6. Mrs. Bell had 30 pennies. She gave $\frac{1}{3}$ of the pennies to Max and $\frac{1}{2}$ of the pennies to Julie.

Max received _____ pennies.

Julie received _____ pennies.

How many pennies did Mrs. Bell have left?

_____ pennies

---

1) SDAP 1.4   2) AF **1.1**   3) NS **1.3**
4) MG **2.0**   5) MG 1.0   6) NS **4.2**

LESSON 12·5 Related Multiplication and Division Facts

Solve each multiplication fact. Use the fact triangles to help you.

Then use the three numbers to write two division facts.

1. $3 \times 7 = \underline{21}$

$\underline{21} \div \underline{7} = \underline{3}$

$\underline{21} \div \underline{3} = \underline{7}$

2. $3 \times 8 = \underline{\hspace{1cm}}$

$\underline{\hspace{1cm}} \div \underline{\hspace{1cm}} = \underline{\hspace{1cm}}$

$\underline{\hspace{1cm}} \div \underline{\hspace{1cm}} = \underline{\hspace{1cm}}$

3. $3 \times 9 = \underline{\hspace{1cm}}$

$\underline{\hspace{1cm}} \div \underline{\hspace{1cm}} = \underline{\hspace{1cm}}$

$\underline{\hspace{1cm}} \div \underline{\hspace{1cm}} = \underline{\hspace{1cm}}$

4. $4 \times 7 = \underline{\hspace{1cm}}$

$\underline{\hspace{1cm}} \div \underline{\hspace{1cm}} = \underline{\hspace{1cm}}$

$\underline{\hspace{1cm}} \div \underline{\hspace{1cm}} = \underline{\hspace{1cm}}$

5. $4 \times 8 = \underline{\hspace{1cm}}$

$\underline{\hspace{1cm}} \div \underline{\hspace{1cm}} = \underline{\hspace{1cm}}$

$\underline{\hspace{1cm}} \div \underline{\hspace{1cm}} = \underline{\hspace{1cm}}$

6. $4 \times 9 = \underline{\hspace{1cm}}$

$\underline{\hspace{1cm}} \div \underline{\hspace{1cm}} = \underline{\hspace{1cm}}$

$\underline{\hspace{1cm}} \div \underline{\hspace{1cm}} = \underline{\hspace{1cm}}$

7. $5 \times 7 = \underline{\hspace{1cm}}$

$\underline{\hspace{1cm}} \div \underline{\hspace{1cm}} = \underline{\hspace{1cm}}$

$\underline{\hspace{1cm}} \div \underline{\hspace{1cm}} = \underline{\hspace{1cm}}$

8. $5 \times 8 = \underline{\hspace{1cm}}$

$\underline{\hspace{1cm}} \div \underline{\hspace{1cm}} = \underline{\hspace{1cm}}$

$\underline{\hspace{1cm}} \div \underline{\hspace{1cm}} = \underline{\hspace{1cm}}$

LESSON 12·5 *Addition Card Draw* Directions

Materials ☐ score sheet from *Math Masters*, p. 446

☐ 4 each of number cards 1–10

☐ 1 each of the number cards 11–20

☐ slate or scratch paper

Players 2

Skill Add 3 numbers

Object of the Game To get the higher total

Directions

Shuffle the cards and place the deck with the numbers facing down. Take turns.

1. Draw the top 3 cards from the deck.

2. Record the numbers on the score sheet. Put the 3 cards in a separate pile.

3. Find the sum. Use your slate or paper to do the computation.

After 3 turns:

4. Check your partner's work. Use a calculator.

5. Find the total of the 3 answers. Write the total on the score sheet. The player with the higher total wins.

Number Sense 2.0; Algebra and Functions 1.1

LESSON 12·5   **Math Boxes**

1. Write the number that is

	10 more	**100 less**
368	_____	_____
4,789	_____	_____
40,870	_____	_____
1,999	_____	_____

2. How many days per week?

_____

How many minutes per hour?

_____

How many hours per day?

_____

How many weeks per year?

_____

MRB 86

3. Shade $\frac{1}{2}$ of the shape. Write the equivalent fraction.

_____

4. Fill in the table.

in	out
1	
6	
10	
	80
	250

Rule
×10

MRB 101

5. The time is

____ : ____.

20 minutes later will be

____ : ____.

15 minutes earlier was

____ : ____.

6. Solve.

Unit

____ − 23 = 17

60 − ____ = 28

49 = ____ − 21

54 = 80 − ____

LESSON 12·6 Animal Bar Graph

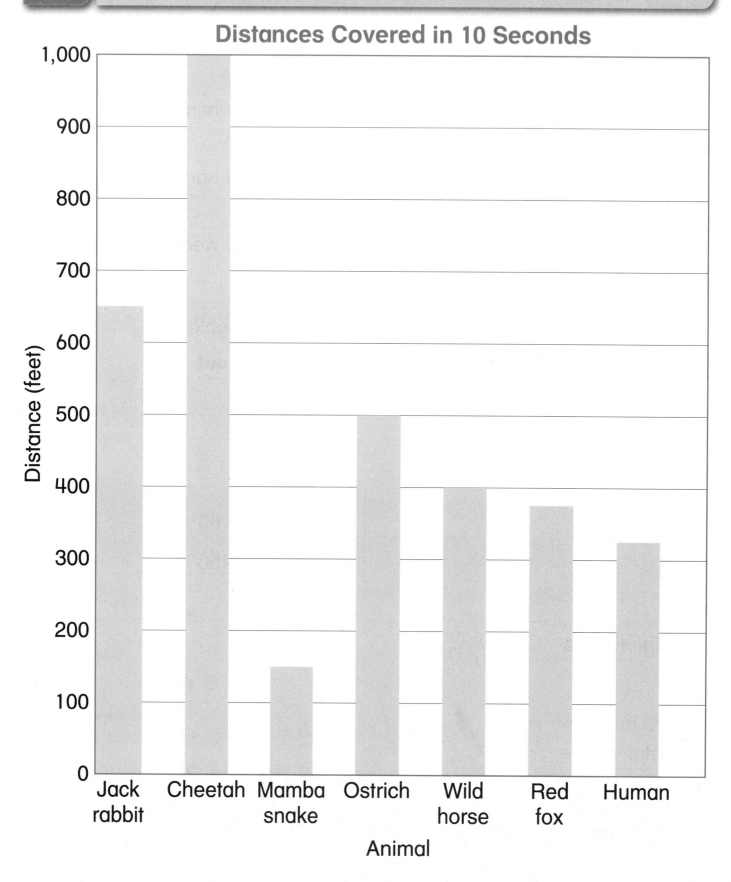

Distances Covered in 10 Seconds

AF 1.3; SDAP 1.1, 1.2, 1.3, 1.4

LESSON 12·6 Interpreting an Animal Bar Graph

1. In the table, list the animals in order of distance covered in 10 seconds. List the animals from the greatest distance to the least distance.

2. Find the middle value of the distances. The middle value is also called the **median.**

   The median is _____ feet.

3. The longest distance is

   _____ feet.

   The shortest distance is

   _____ feet.

Distances Covered in 10 Seconds	
Animal	**Distance**
greatest: _____	_____ ft
_____	_____ ft
_____	_____ ft
_____	_____ ft
_____	_____ ft
_____	_____ ft
least: _____	_____ ft

4. Fill in the comparison diagram with the longest distance and the shortest distance.

Quantity

Quantity
_____ Difference

5. Find the difference between the longest and shortest distances. The difference between the largest and smallest numbers in a data set is called the **range.**

   The range is _____ feet.

LESSON 12·6 Math Boxes

1. Complete the bar graph.

Trees in the State Park

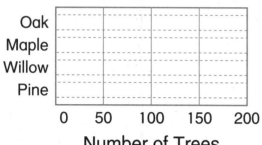

Oak
Maple
Willow
Pine

0   50   100   150   200
Number of Trees

Oak: 100   Maple: 200

Willow: 50   Pine: 150

2. Put parentheses to make each number model true.

$21 = 39 - 10 - 8$

$4 \times 3 + 7 = 40$

$3 \times 5 + 2 = 17$

3. Write <, >, or =.

20,739 _____ 24,596

10,670 _____ 6,670

15,139 _____ 15,264

MRB
9

4. Name the shape.

basketball _____

shoe box

_____

paper towel roll _____

MRB
56 57

5. Draw a shape with an area of 12 square centimeters.

MRB
69

6. A shark swam 80 miles. A seal swam $\frac{1}{2}$ as far as the shark.

How far did the seal swim?

_____ miles

A dolphin swam twice as far as the shark. How far did the dolphin swim?

_____ miles

1) SDAP 1.0   2) AF 1.1   3) NS 1.3
4) MG 2.0   5) MG 1.0   6) NS 4.2

LESSON 12·7 Height Changes

The data in the table show the height of 30 children at ages 7 and 8.
Your teacher will show you how to make a line plot for the data.

Student	Height		Student	Height	
	7 Years	8 Years		7 Years	8 Years
#1	120 cm	123 cm	#16	118 cm	122 cm
#2	132 cm	141 cm	#17	120 cm	126 cm
#3	112 cm	115 cm	#18	141 cm	148 cm
#4	122 cm	126 cm	#19	122 cm	127 cm
#5	118 cm	122 cm	#20	120 cm	126 cm
#6	136 cm	144 cm	#21	120 cm	124 cm
#7	123 cm	127 cm	#22	136 cm	142 cm
#8	127 cm	133 cm	#23	115 cm	118 cm
#9	115 cm	120 cm	#24	122 cm	130 cm
#10	119 cm	125 cm	#25	124 cm	129 cm
#11	122 cm	126 cm	#26	123 cm	127 cm
#12	103 cm	107 cm	#27	131 cm	138 cm
#13	129 cm	136 cm	#28	126 cm	132 cm
#14	124 cm	129 cm	#29	121 cm	123 cm
#15	109 cm	110 cm	#30	118 cm	123 cm

LESSON 12·7   Height Changes *continued*

Use the line plot your class made to make a frequency table
for the data.

Frequency Table	
Change in Height	**Number of Children**
0 cm	
1 cm	
2 cm	
3 cm	
4 cm	
5 cm	
6 cm	
7 cm	
8 cm	
9 cm	
10 cm	

AF 1.3; SDAP **1.0**, 1.2, 1.3, 1.4

LESSON 12·7 Height Changes *continued*

1. Make a bar graph of the data in the frequency table.

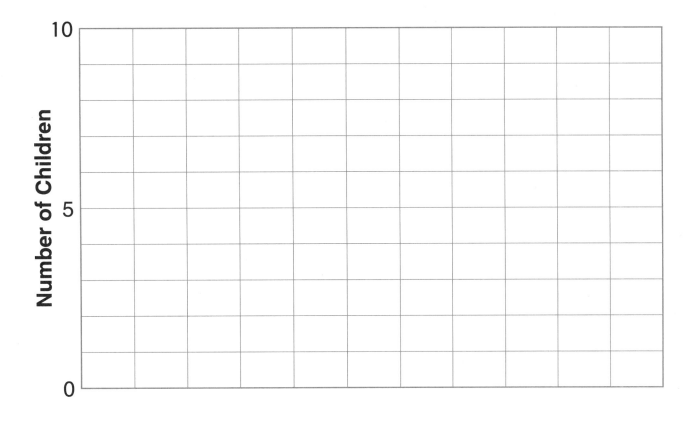

Height Changes (centimeters)

2. The minimum is _____ centimeter(s).

3. The maximum is _____ centimeter(s).

4. The median (the middle value) for the height change data is _____ centimeter(s).

5. The mode (the height change that occurred most often) is _____ centimeter(s).

6. The range is _____ centimeter(s).

LESSON 12·7 · Math Boxes

1. Write another name for each number.

50 tens = _____

32 hundreds = _____

6,240 = 624 _____

12,000 = 12 _____

MRB
10

2. Jim ate dinner in _____.
Fill in the circle next to the best answer.

Ⓐ 2 months

Ⓑ 20 minutes

Ⓒ 2 years

Ⓓ 2 weeks

3. Cross out the fractions that do not belong.

$\frac{1}{2}$

$\frac{2}{3}$, $\frac{3}{5}$, $\frac{4}{8}$,

$\frac{6}{12}$, $\frac{6}{8}$, $\frac{5}{10}$, $\frac{1}{4}$

4. Use counters. Fill in the table.

in	out
4	
9	
7	
	20
	40

Rule
× 4

MRB
101

5. Write the time in hours and minutes.

10 minutes past 12   ____:____

quarter to 11   ____:____

half-past 7   ____:____

25 minutes to 8   ____:____

MRB
82 83

6. Subtract.

$5.44 $5.44
– $0.29   – $3.29

MRB
34 35

1) NS 1.2   2) NS 6.1   3) NS 4.1
4) AF 1.3   5) MG 1.4   6) NS 2.2

LESSON 12·8   **Math Boxes**

1. Write the number. Use your Place-Value Book if you need help.

3 tens = _____

33 tens = _____

333 tens = _____

2. Match.

1 day   14 days

3 days   48 hours

2 weeks   24 hours

2 days   72 hours

3. Write the fractions.

△ △ △ △
△ △ △ △
△ △ △ △

_____ or _____

4. Fill in the table.

Rule
×3

in	out
0	
1	
2	
3	
	12
	30

5. Cross out names that don't belong.

6:15

six fifteen, quarter to 7,

quarter past 6,

15 minutes before 6,

15 minutes after 6

6. Solve.

Unit

$$\begin{array}{r} 687 \\ -\ 409 \\ \hline \end{array}$$ $$\begin{array}{r} 569 \\ -\ 372 \\ \hline \end{array}$$

Table of Equivalencies

Weight

kilogram	1,000 g
pound	16 oz
ton	2,000 lb
1 ounce is about 30 g	

<	is less than
>	is more than
=	is equal to
=	is the same as

Length

kilometer	1,000 m
meter	100 cm or 10 dm
decimeter	10 cm
centimeter	10 mm
foot	12 in.
yard	3 ft or 36 in.
mile	5,280 ft or 1,760 yd
10 cm is about 4 in.	

Time

year	365 or 366 days
year	about 52 weeks
year	12 months
month	28, 29, 30, or 31 days
week	7 days
day	24 hours
hour	60 minutes
minute	60 seconds

Money

(penny)	1¢, or $0.01	Ⓟ
(nickel)	5¢, or $0.05	Ⓝ
(dime)	10¢, or $0.10	Ⓓ
(quarter)	25¢, or $0.25	Ⓠ
(dollar bill)	100¢, or $1.00	$1

Abbreviations

kilometers	km
meters	m
centimeters	cm
miles	mi
feet	ft
yards	yd
inches	in.
tons	T
pounds	lb
ounces	oz
kilograms	kg
grams	g
decimeters	dm
millimeters	mm
pints	pt
quarts	qt
gallons	gal
liters	L
milliliters	mL

Capacity

1 pint = 2 cups
1 quart = 2 pints
1 gallon = 4 quarts
1 liter = 1,000 milliliters

Contents

California Projects

PROJECT 9
Sasha's San Diego Zoo Adventure

CALIFORNIA

Use Sasha's schedule to answer each question.

1. How much time will Sasha spend in the gift shop? _____

2. How many hours will Sasha spend watching the animals eat? _____

3. How many hours will Sasha spend in the park before she eats lunch? _____

4. How many hours in all will Sasha spend eating lunch and dinner? _____

5. How many hours will Sasha spend at the zoo? _____

Sasha's Schedule

9:00 A.M. Arrive at the zoo
Exhibit: Monkey Trails and Forest Tales

10:00 A.M. Ride the Skyfari

12:00 NOON Lunch

1:00 P.M. Petting Paddock

2:00 P.M. Botanical Bus Tour

3:00 P.M. Gift Shop

4:00 P.M. Feed the apes

5:00 P.M. Dinner

6:00 P.M. Visit Flamingo Lagoon and Fern Canyon

7:00 P.M. Watch the hippos feeding

8:00 P.M. Leave the zoo

PROJECT 9

Collin's San Diego Zoo Adventure

CALIFORNIA

Use Collin's schedule to answer each question.

1. How many hours will Collin spend at shows? _____

2. How many hours will the Photo Caravan Safari Tour last? _____

3. How many hours will Collin spend feeding animals? _____

4. How many hours will Collin spend in the zoo after he eats lunch? _____

5. How many hours will Collin spend at the zoo? _____

Collin's Schedule

10:00 A.M. Arrive at the Park
Exhibit: Ituri Forest

11:00 A.M. Ride the Skyfari

12:00 NOON Feed the giraffes

1:00 P.M. Lunch

2:00 P.M. *Frequent Flyers* Bird
Show at the Wild
Animal Park

3:00 P.M. Elephant Show at
the Wild Animal Park

4:00 P.M. Photo Caravan
Safari Tour at the
Wild Animal Park

6:00 P.M. Dinner

7:00 P.M. Balloon Safari at the
Wild Animal Park

8:00 P.M. Leave the Park

PROJECT 9

_____'s Schedule at the Zoo ⟨CALIFORNIA⟩

Start Time

Activity

_____ Arrive at the Park _____

_____ _____

_____ _____

_____ _____

_____ _____

_____ _____

_____ _____

_____ Leave the Park _____

PROJECT 9 **Bar Graph**

Title: _____

Number of Children

0

**PROJECT
9**   **Family Fun Day**

Write times to the hour for each activity.

Start Time	**Activity**
_____	_____
_____	_____
_____	_____
_____	_____
_____	_____
_____	_____
_____	_____
_____	_____
_____	_____

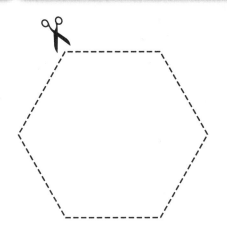

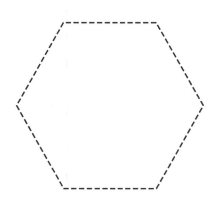

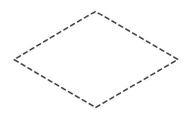

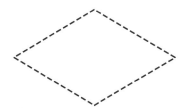

Pattern Blocks

CALIFORNIA

Building a Pagoda

Use pattern blocks to build your own pagoda.

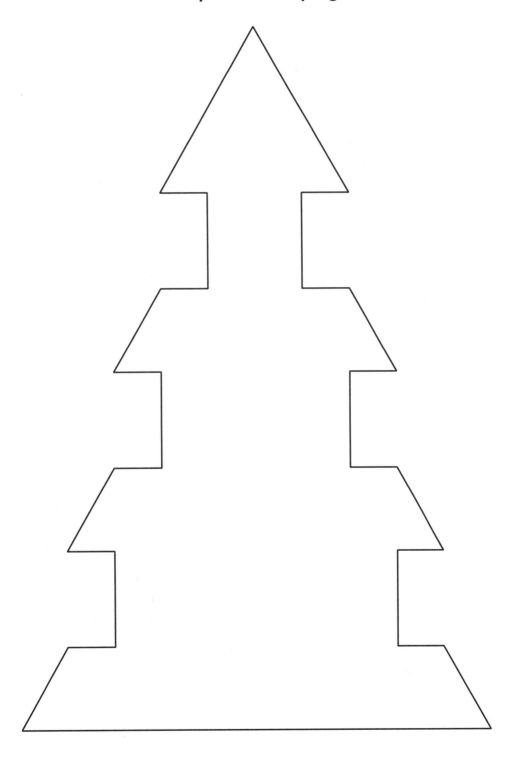

PROJECT 11   Listing Multiples

_____ x 1 = _____   _____ x 6 = _____

_____ x 2 = _____   _____ x 7 = _____

_____ x 3 = _____   _____ x 8 = _____

_____ x 4 = _____   _____ x 9 = _____

_____ x 5 = _____   _____ x 10 = _____

Try This

What pattern do you see in the multiples?

_____

_____

_____

Date _____ Time _____

PROJECT 11

Multiplication Book Pages

_____ X _____ = _____

- -

Date _____ Time _____

PROJECT 11

Multiplication Book Pages

_____ X _____ = _____

Multiplication Fact Power Game Mat

CALIFORNIA

START →

1 × 1	2 × 1	3 × 1	4 × 1	5 × 1	6 × 1	7 × 1	8 × 1	9 × 1	10 × 1
1 × 2	2 × 2	3 × 2	4 × 2	5 × 2	6 × 2	7 × 2	8 × 2	9 × 2	10 × 2
1 × 3	2 × 3	3 × 3	4 × 3	5 × 3	6 × 3	7 × 3	8 × 3	9 × 3	10 × 3
1 × 4	2 × 4	3 × 4	4 × 4	5 × 4	6 × 4	7 × 4	8 × 4	9 × 4	10 × 4
1 × 5	2 × 5	3 × 5	4 × 5	5 × 5	6 × 5	7 × 5	8 × 5	9 × 5	10 × 5
1 × 6	2 × 6	3 × 6	4 × 6	5 × 6	6 × 6	7 × 6	8 × 6	9 × 6	10 × 6
1 × 7	2 × 7	3 × 7	4 × 7	5 × 7	6 × 7	7 × 7	8 × 7	9 × 7	10 × 7
1 × 8	2 × 8	3 × 8	4 × 8	5 × 8	6 × 8	7 × 8	8 × 8	9 × 8	10 × 8
1 × 9	2 × 9	3 × 9	4 × 9	5 × 9	6 × 9	7 × 9	8 × 9	9 × 9	10 × 9
1 ×10	2 ×10	3 ×10	4 ×10	5 ×10	6 ×10	7 ×10	8 ×10	9 ×10	10 ×10

END ←

Number Sense **3.3**

Grid Paper

California Content Standards

The California Mathematics Content Standards describe what every student in California can and needs to learn in mathematics. These standards are identified at the bottom of each of your journal pages and are listed here for your reference. The oval identifies the key standards for this grade level.

Number Sense

Number Sense 1.0 Students understand the relationship between numbers, quantities, and place value in whole numbers up to 1,000:

Number Sense 1.1 Count, read, and write whole numbers to 1,000 and identify the place value for each digit.

Number Sense 1.2 Use words, models, and expanded forms (e.g., 45 = 4 tens + 5) to represent numbers (to 1,000).

Number Sense 1.3 Order and compare whole numbers to 1,000 by using the symbols <, =, >.

Number Sense 2.0 Students estimate, calculate, and solve problems involving addition and subtraction of two- and three-digit numbers:

Number Sense 2.1 Understand and use the inverse relationship between addition and subtraction (e.g., an opposite number sentence for 8 + 6 = 14 is 14 − 6 = 8) to solve problems and check solutions.

Number Sense 2.2 Find the sum or difference of two whole numbers up to three digits long.

Number Sense 2.3 Use mental arithmetic to find the sum or difference of two two-digit numbers.

Number Sense 3.0 Students model and solve simple problems involving multiplication and division:

Number Sense 3.1 Use repeated addition, arrays, and counting by multiples to do multiplication.

Number Sense 3.2 Use repeated subtraction, equal sharing, and forming equal groups with remainders to do division.

Number Sense 3.3 Know the multiplication tables of 2s, 5s, and 10s (to "times 10") and commit them to memory.

Number Sense 4.0 Students understand that fractions and decimals may refer to parts of a set and parts of a whole:

Number Sense 4.1 Recognize, name, and compare unit fractions from $\frac{1}{12}$ to $\frac{1}{2}$.

Number Sense 4.2 Recognize fractions of a whole and parts of a group (e.g., one-fourth of a pie, two-thirds of 15 balls).

Number Sense 4.3 Know that when all fractional parts are included, such as four-fourths, the result is equal to the whole and to one.

Number Sense 5.0 Students model and solve problems by representing, adding, and subtracting amounts of money:

Number Sense 5.1 Solve problems using combinations of coins and bills.

Number Sense 5.2 Know and use the decimal notation and the dollar and cent symbols for money.

Number Sense 6.0 Students use estimation strategies in computation and problem solving that involve numbers that use the ones, tens, hundreds, and thousands places:

Number Sense 6.1 Recognize when an estimate is reasonable in measurements (e.g., closest inch).

Algebra and Functions

Algebra and Functions 1.0 Students model, represent, and interpret number relationships to create and solve problems involving addition and subtraction:

Algebra and Functions 1.1 Use the commutative and associative rules to simplify mental calculations and to check results.

Algebra and Functions 1.2 Relate problem situations to number sentences involving addition and subtraction.

Algebra and Functions 1.3 Solve addition and subtraction problems by using data from simple charts, picture graphs, and number sentences.

Measurement and Geometry

Measurement and Geometry 1.0 Students understand that measurement is accomplished by identifying a unit of measure, iterating (repeating) that unit, and comparing it to the item to be measured:

Measurement and Geometry 1.1 Measure the length of objects by iterating (repeating) a nonstandard or standard unit.

Measurement and Geometry 1.2 Use different units to measure the same object and predict whether the measure will be greater or smaller when a different unit is used.

Measurement and Geometry 1.3 Measure the length of an object to the nearest inch and/or centimeter.

Measurement and Geometry 1.4 Tell time to the nearest quarter hour and know relationships of time (e.g., minutes in an hour, days in a month, weeks in a year).

Measurement and Geometry 1.5 Determine the duration of intervals of time in hours (e.g., 11:00 a.m. to 4:00 p.m.).

Measurement and Geometry 2.0 Students identify and describe the attributes of common figures in the plane and of common objects in space:

Measurement and Geometry 2.1 Describe and classify plane and solid geometric shapes (e.g., circle, triangle, square, rectangle, sphere, pyramid, cube, rectangular prism) according to the number and shape of faces, edges, and vertices.

Measurement and Geometry 2.2 Put shapes together and take them apart to form other shapes (e.g., two congruent right triangles can be arranged to form a rectangle).

Statistics, Data Analysis, and Probability

Statistics, Data Analysis, and Probability 1.0 Students collect numerical data and record, organize, display, and interpret the data on bar graphs and other representations:

Statistics, Data Analysis, and Probability 1.1 Record numerical data in systematic ways, keeping track of what has been counted.

Statistics, Data Analysis, and Probability 1.2 Represent the same data set in more than one way (e.g., bar graphs and charts with tallies).

Statistics, Data Analysis, and Probability 1.3 Identify features of data sets (range and mode).

Statistics, Data Analysis, and Probability 1.4 Ask and answer simple questions related to data representations.

Statistics, Data Analysis, and Probability 2.0 Students demonstrate an understanding of patterns and how patterns grow and describe them in general ways:

Statistics, Data Analysis, and Probability 2.1 Recognize, describe, and extend patterns and determine a next term in linear patterns (e.g., 4, 8, 12, ...; the number of ears on one horse, two horses, three horses, four horses).

Statistics, Data Analysis, and Probability 2.2 Solve problems involving simple number patterns.

Mathematical Reasoning

Mathematical Reasoning 1.0 Students make decisions about how to set up a problem:

Mathematical Reasoning 1.1 Determine the approach, materials, and strategies to be used.

Mathematical Reasoning 1.2 Use tools, such as manipulatives or sketches, to model problems.

Mathematical Reasoning 2.0 Students solve problems and justify their reasoning:

Mathematical Reasoning 2.1 Defend the reasoning used and justify the procedures selected.

Mathematical Reasoning 2.2 Make precise calculations and check the validity of the results in the context of the problem.

Mathematical Reasoning 3.0 Students note connections between one problem and another.

California Content Standards for Math Boxes

Math Boxes 7•1

1. **Mathematical Reasoning 2.0** Students solve problems and justify their reasoning.
2. **Algebra and Functions 1.3** Solve addition and subtraction problems by using data from simple charts, picture graphs, and number sentences.
3. **Number Sense 3.1** Use repeated addition, arrays, and counting by multiples to do multiplication.
4. **Statistics, Data Analysis, and Probability 1.3** Identify features of data sets (range and mode).
5. **Number Sense 6.1** Recognize when an estimate is reasonable in measurements (e.g., closest inch).
6. **Number Sense 4.2** Recognize fractions of a whole and parts of a group (e.g., one-fourth of a pie, two-thirds of 15 balls).

Math Boxes 7•2

1. **Number Sense 3.2** Use repeated subtraction, equal sharing, and forming equal groups with remainders to do division.
2. **Number Sense 2.0** Students estimate, calculate, and solve problems involving addition and subtraction of two- and three-digit numbers.
3. **Statistics, Data Analysis, and Probability 2.1** Recognize, describe, and extend patterns and determine a next term in linear patterns (e.g., 4, 8, 12 . . .; the number of ears on one horse, two horses, three horses, four horses).
4. **Mathematical Reasoning 1.2** Use tools, such as manipulatives or sketches, to model problems.
5. **Algebra and Functions 1.3** Solve addition and subtraction problems by using data from simple charts, picture graphs, and number sentences.
6. **Number Sense 4.1** Recognize, name, and compare unit fractions from $\frac{1}{12}$ to $\frac{1}{2}$.

Math Boxes 7•3

1. **Mathematical Reasoning 2.0** Students solve problems and justify their reasoning.
2. **Algebra and Functions 1.3** Solve addition and subtraction problems by using data from simple charts, picture graphs, and number sentences.
3. **Number Sense 3.1** Use repeated addition, arrays, and counting by multiples to do multiplication.
4. **Statistics, Data Analysis, and Probability 1.3** Identify features of data sets (range and mode).
5. **Number Sense 3.0** Students model and solve simple problems involving multiplication and division.
6. **Number Sense 4.1** Recognize, name, and compare unit fractions from $\frac{1}{12}$ to $\frac{1}{2}$.

Math Boxes 7•4

1. **Number Sense 3.2** Use repeated subtraction, equal sharing, and forming equal groups with remainders to do division.
2. **Algebra and Functions 1.3** Solve addition and subtraction problems by using data from simple charts, picture graphs, and number sentences.
3. **Statistics, Data Analysis, and Probability 2.1** Recognize, describe, and extend patterns and determine a next term in linear patterns (e.g., 4, 8, 12 . . .; the number of ears on one horse, two horses, three horses, four horses).
4. **Mathematical Reasoning 1.2** Use tools, such as manipulatives or sketches, to model problems.
5. **Algebra and Functions 1.3** Solve addition and subtraction problems by using data from simple charts, picture graphs, and number sentences.
6. **Number Sense 4.1** Recognize, name, and compare unit fractions from $\frac{1}{12}$ to $\frac{1}{2}$.

Math Boxes 7•5

1. **Measurement and Geometry 1.4** Tell time to the nearest quarter hour and know relationships of time (e.g., minutes in an hour, days in a month, weeks in a year).
2. **Statistics, Data Analysis, and Probability 1.4** Ask and answer simple questions related to data representations.
3. **Number Sense 3.1** Use repeated addition, arrays, and counting by multiples to do multiplication.
4. **Statistics, Data Analysis, and Probability 2.1** Recognize, describe, and extend patterns and determine a next term in linear patterns (e.g., 4, 8, 12 . . .; the number of ears on one horse, two horses, three horses, four horses).
5. **Measurement and Geometry 2.0** Students identify and describe the attributes of common figures in the plane and of common objects in space.
6. **Number Sense 4.1** Recognize, name, and compare unit fractions from $\frac{1}{12}$ to $\frac{1}{2}$.

Math Boxes 7•6

1. **Number Sense 5.0** Students model and solve problems by representing, adding, and subtracting amounts of money.
2. **Number Sense 3.1** Use repeated addition, arrays, and counting by multiples to do multiplication.
3. **Measurement and Geometry 1.0** Students understand that measurement is accomplished by identifying a unit of measure, iterating (repeating) that unit, and comparing it to the item to be measured.
4. **Statistics, Data Analysis, and Probability 1.3** Identify features of data sets (range and mode).
5. **Number Sense 6.0** Students use estimation strategies in computation and problem solving that involve numbers that use the ones, tens, hundreds, and thousands places.
6. **Number Sense 4.1** Recognize, name, and compare unit fractions from $\frac{1}{12}$ to $\frac{1}{2}$.

Math Boxes 7•7

1. **Measurement and Geometry 1.4** Tell time to the nearest quarter hour and know relationships of time (e.g., minutes in an hour, days in a month, weeks in a year).

2. **Statistics, Data Analysis, and Probability 1.3** Identify features of data sets (range and mode).

3. **Number Sense 3.1** Use repeated addition, arrays, and counting by multiples to do multiplication.

4. **Statistics, Data Analysis, and Probability 2.1** Recognize, describe, and extend patterns and determine a next term in linear patterns (e.g., 4, 8, 12 . . .; the number of ears on one horse, two horses, three horses, four horses).

5. **Measurement and Geometry 2.1** Describe and classify plane and solid geometric shapes (e.g., circle, triangle, square, rectangle, sphere, pyramid, cube, rectangular prism) according to the number and shape of faces, edges, and vertices

6. **Number Sense 4.1** Recognize, name, and compare unit fractions from $\frac{1}{12}$ to $\frac{1}{2}$.

Math Boxes 7•8

1. **Number Sense 5.0** Students model and solve problems by representing, adding, and subtracting amounts of money.

2. **Number Sense 3.1** Use repeated addition, arrays, and counting by multiples to do multiplication.

3. **Measurement and Geometry 1.0** Students understand that measurement is accomplished by identifying a unit of measure, iterating (repeating) that unit, and comparing it to the item to be measured.

4. **Statistics, Data Analysis, and Probability 1.3** Identify features of data sets (range and mode).

5. **Number Sense 6.0** Students use estimation strategies in computation and problem solving that involve numbers that use the ones, tens, hundreds, and thousands places.

6. **Number Sense 4.1** Recognize, name, and compare unit fractions from $\frac{1}{12}$ to $\frac{1}{2}$.

Math Boxes 7•9

1. **Number Sense 4.2** Recognize fractions of a whole and parts of a group (e.g., one-fourth of a pie, two-thirds of 15 balls).

2. **Number Sense 4.1** Recognize, name, and compare unit fractions from $\frac{1}{12}$ to $\frac{1}{2}$.

3. **Mathematical Reasoning 1.0** Students make decisions about how to set up a problem.

4. **Number Sense 4.1** Recognize, name, and compare unit fractions from $\frac{1}{12}$ to $\frac{1}{2}$.

5. **Number Sense 4.2** Recognize fractions of a whole and parts of a group (e.g., one-fourth of a pie, two-thirds of 15 balls).

6. **Number Sense 4.0** Students understand that fractions and decimals may refer to parts of a set and parts of a whole.

Math Boxes 8•1

1. **Number Sense 4.1** Recognize, name, and compare unit fractions from $\frac{1}{12}$ to $\frac{1}{2}$.

2. **Mathematical Reasoning 1.2** Use tools, such as manipulatives or sketches, to model problems.

3. **Statistics, Data Analysis, and Probability 2.2** Solve problems involving simple number patterns.

4. **Number Sense 5.1** Solve problems using combinations of coins and bills.

5. **Mathematical Reasoning 2.0** Students solve problems and justify their reasoning.

6. **Number Sense 6.1** Recognize when an estimate is reasonable in measurements (e.g., closest inch).

Math Boxes 8•2

1. **Statistics, Data Analysis, and Probability 2.1** Recognize, describe, and extend patterns and determine a next term in linear patterns (e.g., 4, 8, 12 . . .; the number of ears on one horse, two horses, three horses, four horses).

2. **Measurement and Geometry 1.4** Tell time to the nearest quarter hour and know relationships of time (e.g., minutes in an hour, days in a month, weeks in a year).

3. **Number Sense 1.1** Count, read, and write whole numbers to 1,000 and identify the place value for each digit.

4. **Number Sense 4.2** Recognize fractions of a whole and parts of a group (e.g., one-fourth of a pie, two-thirds of 15 balls).

5. **Measurement and Geometry 1.3** Measure the length of an object to the nearest inch and/or centimeter.

6. **Measurement and Geometry 1.0** Students understand that measurement is accomplished by identifying a unit of measure, iterating (repeating) that unit, and comparing it to the item to be measured.

Math Boxes 8•3

1. **Number Sense 4.1** Recognize, name, and compare unit fractions from $\frac{1}{12}$ to $\frac{1}{2}$.

2. **Mathematical Reasoning 1.2** Use tools, such as manipulatives or sketches, to model problems.

3. **Statistics, Data Analysis, and Probability 2.2** Solve problems involving simple number patterns.

4. **Number Sense 5.1** Solve problems using combinations of coins and bills.

5. **Mathematical Reasoning 2.0** Students solve problems and justify their reasoning.

6. **Number Sense 6.1** Recognize when an estimate is reasonable in measurements (e.g., closest inch).

Math Boxes 8•4

1. **Statistics, Data Analysis, and Probability 2.1** Recognize, describe, and extend patterns and determine a next term in linear patterns (e.g., 4, 8, 12 . . .; the number of ears on one horse, two horses, three horses, four horses).

2. **Measurement and Geometry 1.4** Tell time to the nearest quarter hour and know relationships of time (e.g., minutes in an hour, days in a month, weeks in a year).

CA20

Math Boxes 8•4 *cont.*

3. **Number Sense 1.1** Count, read, and write whole numbers to 1,000 and identify the place value for each digit.

4. **Number Sense 4.2** Recognize fractions of a whole and parts of a group (e.g., one-fourth of a pie, two-thirds of 15 balls).

5. **Measurement and Geometry 1.3** Measure the length of an object to the nearest inch and/or centimeter.

6. **Measurement and Geometry 1.0** Students understand that measurement is accomplished by identifying a unit of measure, iterating (repeating) that unit, and comparing it to the item to be measured.

Math Boxes 8•5

1. **Statistics, Data Analysis, and Probability 1.3** Identify features of data sets (range and mode).

2. **Number Sense 4.2** Recognize fractions of a whole and parts of a group (e.g., one-fourth of a pie, two-thirds of 15 balls).

3. **Statistics, Data Analysis, and Probability 2.1** Recognize, describe, and extend patterns and determine a next term in linear patterns (e.g., 4, 8, 12 . . .; the number of ears on one horse, two horses, three horses, four horses).

4. **Algebra and Functions 1.2** Relate problem situations to number sentences involving addition and subtraction.

5. **Measurement and Geometry 1.3** Measure the length of an object to the nearest inch and/or centimeter.

6. **Measurement and Geometry 1.0** Students understand that measurement is accomplished by identifying a unit of measure, iterating (repeating) that unit, and comparing it to the item to be measured.

Math Boxes 8•6

1. **Statistics, Data Analysis, and Probability 2.1** Recognize, describe, and extend patterns and determine a next term in linear patterns (e.g., 4, 8, 12 . . .; the number of ears on one horse, two horses, three horses, four horses).

2. **Measurement and Geometry 1.4** Tell time to the nearest quarter hour and know relationships of time (e.g., minutes in an hour, days in a month, weeks in a year).

3. **Number Sense 1.1** Count, read, and write whole numbers to 1,000 and identify the place value for each digit.

4. **Number Sense 4.2** Recognize fractions of a whole and parts of a group (e.g., one-fourth of a pie, two-thirds of 15 balls).

5. **Number Sense 6.1** Recognize when an estimate is reasonable in measurements (e.g., closest inch).

6. **Measurement and Geometry 1.0** Students understand that measurement is accomplished by identifying a unit of measure, iterating (repeating) that unit, and comparing it to the item to be measured.

Math Boxes 8•7

1. **Statistics, Data Analysis, and Probability 1.3** Identify features of data sets (range and mode).

2. **Number Sense 4.2** Recognize fractions of a whole and parts of a group (e.g., one-fourth of a pie, two-thirds of 15 balls).

3. **Statistics, Data Analysis, and Probability 2.2** Solve problems involving simple number patterns.

4. **Algebra and Functions 1.2** Relate problem situations to number sentences involving addition and subtraction.

5. **Measurement and Geometry 1.3** Measure the length of an object to the nearest inch and/or centimeter.

6. **Measurement and Geometry 1.0** Students understand that measurement is accomplished by identifying a unit of measure, iterating (repeating) that unit, and comparing it to the item to be measured.

Math Boxes 8•8

1. **Number Sense 6.1** Recognize when an estimate is reasonable in measurements (e.g., closest inch).

2. **Mathematical Reasoning 1.1** Determine the approach, materials, and strategies to be used.

3. **Measurement and Geometry 1.3** Measure the length of an object to the nearest inch and/or centimeter.

4. **Measurement and Geometry 1.3** Measure the length of an object to the nearest inch and/or centimeter.

5. **Number Sense 6.1** Recognize when an estimate is reasonable in measurements (e.g., closest inch).

6. **Measurement and Geometry 1.0** Students understand that measurement is accomplished by identifying a unit of measure, iterating (repeating) that unit, and comparing it to the item to be measured.

Math Boxes 9•1

1. **Number Sense 3.1** Use repeated addition, arrays, and counting by multiples to do multiplication.

2. **Number Sense 1.3** Order and compare whole numbers to 1,000 by using the symbols $<$, $=$, $>$.

3. **Measurement and Geometry 2.0** Students identify and describe the attributes of common figures in the plane and of common objects in space.

4. **Statistics, Data Analysis, and Probability 1.3** Identify features of data sets (range and mode).

5. **Mathematical Reasoning 1.2** Use tools, such as manipulatives or sketches, to model problems.

6. **Number Sense 5.1** Solve problems using combinations of coins and bills.

Math Boxes 9•2

1. **Statistics, Data Analysis, and Probability 2.1** Recognize, describe, and extend patterns and determine a next term in linear patterns (e.g., 4, 8, 12 . . .; the number of ears on one horse, two horses, three horses, four horses).

2. **Measurement and Geometry 1.3** Measure the length of an object to the nearest inch and/or centimeter.

3. **Algebra and Functions 1.0** Students model, represent, and interpret number relationships to create and solve problems involving addition and subtraction.

4. **Mathematical Reasoning 2.0** Students solve problems and justify their reasoning.

CA21

Math Boxes 9•2 cont.

5. **Number Sense 3.1** Use repeated addition, arrays, and counting by multiples to do multiplication.

6. **Number Sense 5.0** Students model and solve problems by representing, adding, and subtracting amounts of money.

Math Boxes 9•3

1. **Number Sense 3.1** Use repeated addition, arrays, and counting by multiples to do multiplication.

2. **Number Sense 1.3** Order and compare whole numbers to 1,000 by using the symbols $<$, $-$, $>$.

3. **Measurement and Geometry 2.1** Describe and classify plane and solid geometric shapes (e.g., circle, triangle, square, rectangle, sphere, pyramid, cube, rectangular prism) according to the number and shape of faces, edges, and vertices.

4. **Statistics, Data Analysis, and Probability 1.3** Identify features of data sets (range and mode).

5. **Mathematical Reasoning 1.2** Use tools, such as manipulatives or sketches, to model problems.

6. **Number Sense 5.1** Solve problems using combinations of coins and bills.

Math Boxes 9•4

1. **Statistics, Data Analysis, and Probability 2.1** Recognize, describe, and extend patterns and determine a next term in linear patterns (e.g., 4, 8, 12 . . .; the number of ears on one horse, two horses, three horses, four horses).

2. **Measurement and Geometry 1.3** Measure the length of an object to the nearest inch and/or centimeter.

3. **Algebra and Functions 1.0** Students model, represent, and interpret number relationships to create and solve problems involving addition and subtraction.

4. **Mathematical Reasoning 2.0** Students solve problems and justify their reasoning.

5. **Number Sense 3.1** Use repeated addition, arrays, and counting by multiples to do multiplication.

6. **Number Sense 5.0** Students model and solve problems by representing, adding, and subtracting amounts of money.

Math Boxes 9•5

1. **Number Sense 4.1** Recognize, name, and compare unit fractions from $\frac{1}{12}$ to $\frac{1}{2}$.

2. **Number Sense 1.0** Students understand the relationship between numbers, quantities, and place value in whole numbers up to 1,000.

3. **Number Sense 3.2** Use repeated subtraction, equal sharing, and forming equal groups with remainders to do division.

4. **Number Sense 5.2** Know and use the decimal notation and the dollar and cent symbols for money.

5. **Number Sense 2.2** Find the sum or difference of two whole numbers up to three digits long.

6. **Number Sense 1.1** Count, read, and write whole numbers to 1,000 and identify the place value for each digit.

Math Boxes 9•6

1. **Number Sense 1.2** Use words, models, and expanded forms (e.g., 45 = 4 tens + 5) to represent numbers (to 1,000).

2. **Statistics, Data Analysis, and Probability 2.2** Solve problems involving simple number patterns.

3. **Number Sense 2.2** Find the sum or difference of two whole numbers up to three digits long.

4. **Measurement and Geometry 1.0** Students understand that measurement is accomplished by identifying a unit of measure, iterating (repeating) that unit, and comparing it to the item to be measured.

5. **Number Sense 2.0** Students estimate, calculate, and solve problems involving addition and subtraction of two- and three-digit numbers.

6. **Number Sense 5.1** Solve problems using combinations of coins and bills.

Math Boxes 9•7

1. **Number Sense 4.1** Recognize, name, and compare unit fractions from $\frac{1}{12}$ to $\frac{1}{2}$.

2. **Number Sense 1.0** Students understand the relationship between numbers, quantities, and place value in whole numbers up to 1,000.

3. **Number Sense 3.2** Use repeated subtraction, equal sharing, and forming equal groups with remainders to do division.

4. **Number Sense 5.2** Know and use the decimal notation and the dollar and cent symbols for money.

5. **Number Sense 2.2** Find the sum or difference of two whole numbers up to three digits long.

6. **Number Sense 1.1** Count, read, and write whole numbers to 1,000 and identify the place value for each digit.

Math Boxes 9•8

1. **Number Sense 1.2** Use words, models, and expanded forms (e.g., 45 = 4 tens + 5) to represent numbers (to 1,000).

2. **Statistics, Data Analysis, and Probability 2.2** Solve problems involving simple number patterns.

3. **Number Sense 2.2** Find the sum or difference of two whole numbers up to three digits long.

4. **Measurement and Geometry 1.0** Students understand that measurement is accomplished by identifying a unit of measure, iterating (repeating) that unit, and comparing it to the item to be measured.

5. **Number Sense 2.0** Students estimate, calculate, and solve problems involving addition and subtraction of two- and three-digit numbers.

6. **Number Sense 5.1** Solve problems using combinations of coins and bills.

Math Boxes 9•9

1. **Number Sense 4.1** Recognize, name, and compare unit fractions from $\frac{1}{12}$ to $\frac{1}{2}$.

2. **Number Sense 1.0** Students understand the relationship between numbers, quantities, and place value in whole numbers up to 1,000.

Math Boxes 9•9 cont.

3. **Number Sense 3.2** Use repeated subtraction, equal sharing, and forming equal groups with remainders to do division.

4. **Algebra and Functions 1.2** Relate problem situations to number sentences involving addition and subtraction.

5. **Number Sense 2.2** Find the sum or difference of two whole numbers up to three digits long.

6. **Number Sense 1.1** Count, read, and write whole numbers to 1,000 and identify the place value for each digit.

Math Boxes 9•10

1. **Number Sense 3.0** Students model and solve simple problems involving multiplication and division.

2. **Number Sense 1.1** Count, read, and write whole numbers to 1,000 and identify the place value for each digit.

3. **Number Sense 5.1** Solve problems using combinations of coins and bills.

4. **Number Sense 5.1** Solve problems using combinations of coins and bills.

5. **Number Sense 2.0** Students estimate, calculate, and solve problems involving addition and subtraction of two- and three-digit numbers.

6. **Number Sense 5.0** Students model and solve problems by representing, adding, and subtracting amounts of money.

Math Boxes 10•1

1. **Number Sense 5.1** Solve problems using combinations of coins and bills.

2. **Number Sense 4.2** Recognize fractions of a whole and parts of a group (e.g., one-fourth of a pie, two-thirds of 15 balls).

3. **Statistics, Data Analysis, and Probability 2.2** Solve problems involving simple number patterns.

4. **Number Sense 1.0** Students understand the relationship between numbers, quantities, and place value in whole numbers up to 1,000.

5. **Mathematical Reasoning 1.2** Use tools, such as manipulatives or sketches, to model problems.

6. **Number Sense 3.1** Use repeated addition, arrays, and counting by multiples to do multiplication.

Math Boxes 10•2

1. **Number Sense 1.3** Order and compare whole numbers to 1,000 by using the symbols $<$, $=$, $>$.

2. **Number Sense 6.0** Students use estimation strategies in computation and problem solving that involve numbers that use the ones, tens, hundreds, and thousands places.

3. **Statistics, Data Analysis, and Probability 1.3** Identify features of data sets (range and mode).

4. **Measurement and Geometry 1.0** Students understand that measurement is accomplished by identifying a unit of measure, iterating (repeating) that unit, and comparing it to the item to be measured.

5. **Measurement and Geometry 1.4** Tell time to the nearest quarter hour and know relationships of time (e.g., minutes in an hour, days in a month, weeks in a year).

6. **Number Sense 3.2** Use repeated subtraction, equal sharing, and forming equal groups with remainders to do division.

Math Boxes 10•3

1. **Number Sense 5.1** Solve problems using combinations of coins and bills.

2. **Number Sense 4.2** Recognize fractions of a whole and parts of a group (e.g., one-fourth of a pie, two-thirds of 15 balls).

3. **Statistics, Data Analysis, and Probability 2.2** Solve problems involving simple number patterns.

4. **Number Sense 1.0** Students understand the relationship between numbers, quantities, and place value in whole numbers up to 1,000.

5. **Measurement and Geometry 1.0** Students understand that measurement is accomplished by identifying a unit of measure, iterating (repeating) that unit, and comparing it to the item to be measured.

6. **Number Sense 3.1** Use repeated addition, arrays, and counting by multiples to do multiplication.

Math Boxes 10•4

1. **Number Sense 1.3** Order and compare whole numbers to 1,000 by using the symbols $<$, $=$, $>$.

2. **Number Sense 6.0** Students use estimation strategies in computation and problem solving that involve numbers that use the ones, tens, hundreds, and thousands places.

3. **Statistics, Data Analysis, and Probability 1.3** Identify features of data sets (range and mode).

4. **Measurement and Geometry 1.0** Students understand that measurement is accomplished by identifying a unit of measure, iterating (repeating) that unit, and comparing it to the item to be measured.

5. **Measurement and Geometry 1.4** Tell time to the nearest quarter hour and know relationships of time (e.g., minutes in an hour, days in a month, weeks in a year).

6. **Number Sense 3.2** Use repeated subtraction, equal sharing, and forming equal groups with remainders to do division.

Math Boxes 10•5

1. **Number Sense 5.0** Students model and solve problems by representing, adding, and subtracting amounts of money.

2. **Number Sense 4.2** Recognize fractions of a whole and parts of a group (e.g., one-fourth of a pie, two-thirds of 15 balls).

3. **Algebra and Functions 1.3** Solve addition and subtraction problems by using data from simple charts, picture graphs, and number sentences.

4. **Number Sense 1.0** Students understand the relationship between numbers, quantities, and place value in whole numbers up to 1,000.

5. **Measurement and Geometry 1.0** Students understand that measurement is accomplished by identifying a unit of measure, iterating (repeating) that unit, and comparing it to the item to be measured.

Math Boxes 10◆5 cont.

6. **Number Sense (3.2)** Use repeated subtraction, equal sharing, and forming equal groups with remainders to do division.

Math Boxes 10◆6

1. **Number Sense 1.2** Use words, models, and expanded forms (e.g., 45 = 4 tens + 5) to represent numbers (to 1,000).
2. **Number Sense (5.1)** Solve problems using combinations of coins and bills.
3. **Measurement and Geometry 1.0** Students understand that measurement is accomplished by identifying a unit of measure, iterating (repeating) that unit, and comparing it to the item to be measured.
4. **Number Sense 5.0** Students model and solve problems by representing, adding, and subtracting amounts of money.
5. **Measurement and Geometry (2.0)** Students identify and describe the attributes of common figures in the plane and of common objects in space.
6. **Number Sense (3.1)** Use repeated addition, arrays, and counting by multiples to do multiplication.

Math Boxes 10◆7

1. **Mathematical Reasoning 1.2** Use tools, such as manipulatives or sketches, to model problems.
2. **Number Sense (4.2)** Recognize fractions of a whole and parts of a group (e.g., one-fourth of a pie, two-thirds of 15 balls).
3. **Number Sense (5.2)** Know and use the decimal notation and the dollar and cent symbols for money.
4. **Algebra and Functions 1.3** Solve addition and subtraction problems by using data from simple charts, picture graphs, and number sentences.
5. **Measurement and Geometry 1.4** Tell time to the nearest quarter hour and know relationships of time (e.g., minutes in an hour, days in a month, weeks in a year).
6. **Number Sense (3.2)** Use repeated subtraction, equal sharing, and forming equal groups with remainders to do division.

Math Boxes 10◆8

1. **Number Sense 1.2** Use words, models, and expanded forms (e.g., 45 = 4 tens + 5) to represent numbers (to 1,000).
2. **Number Sense 5.0** Students model and solve problems by representing, adding, and subtracting amounts of money.
3. **Algebra and Functions 1.0** Students model, represent, and interpret number relationships to create and solve problems involving addition and subtraction.
4. **Number Sense 5.0** Students model and solve problems by representing, adding, and subtracting amounts of money.
5. **Measurement and Geometry (2.0)** Students identify and describe the attributes of common figures in the plane and of common objects in space.
6. **Number Sense (3.1)** Use repeated addition, arrays, and counting by multiples to do multiplication.

Math Boxes 10◆9

1. **Mathematical Reasoning 1.2** Use tools, such as manipulatives or sketches, to model problems.
2. **Number Sense (4.2)** Recognize fractions of a whole and parts of a group (e.g., one-fourth of a pie, two-thirds of 15 balls).
3. **Number Sense (5.2)** Know and use the decimal notation and the dollar and cent symbols for money.
4. **Algebra and Functions 1.3** Solve addition and subtraction problems by using data from simple charts, picture graphs, and number sentences.
5. **Measurement and Geometry 1.4** Tell time to the nearest quarter hour and know relationships of time (e.g., minutes in an hour, days in a month, weeks in a year).
6. **Number Sense (3.2)** Use repeated subtraction, equal sharing, and forming equal groups with remainders to do division.

Math Boxes 10◆10

1. **Number Sense (1.1)** Count, read, and write whole numbers to 1,000 and identify the place value for each digit.
2. **Number Sense (5.1)** Solve problems using combinations of coins and bills.
3. **Measurement and Geometry 1.0** Students understand that measurement is accomplished by identifying a unit of measure, iterating (repeating) that unit, and comparing it to the item to be measured.
4. **Number Sense 5.0** Students model and solve problems by representing, adding, and subtracting amounts of money.
5. **Measurement and Geometry (2.0)** Students identify and describe the attributes of common figures in the plane and of common objects in space.
6. **Number Sense (3.1)** Use repeated addition, arrays, and counting by multiples to do multiplication.

Math Boxes 10◆11

1. **Mathematical Reasoning 1.2** Use tools, such as manipulatives or sketches, to model problems.
2. **Number Sense (4.2)** Recognize fractions of a whole and parts of a group (e.g., one-fourth of a pie, two-thirds of 15 balls).
3. **Number Sense (5.2)** Know and use the decimal notation and the dollar and cent symbols for money.
4. **Algebra and Functions 1.3** Solve addition and subtraction problems by using data from simple charts, picture graphs, and number sentences.
5. **Measurement and Geometry 1.4** Tell time to the nearest quarter hour and know relationships of time (e.g., minutes in an hour, days in a month, weeks in a year).
6. **Number Sense (3.2)** Use repeated subtraction, equal sharing, and forming equal groups with remainders to do division.

Math Boxes 10◆12

1. **Number Sense (3.1)** Use repeated addition, arrays, and counting by multiples to do multiplication.
2. **Number Sense (3.1)** Use repeated addition, arrays, and counting by multiples to do multiplication.

CA24

Math Boxes 10✦12 *cont.*

3. Number Sense **3.2** Use repeated subtraction, equal sharing, and forming equal groups with remainders to do division.

4. Number Sense **3.1** Use repeated addition, arrays, and counting by multiples to do multiplication.

5. Number Sense **3.1** Use repeated addition, arrays, and counting by multiples to do multiplication.

6. Number Sense **3.2** Use repeated subtraction, equal sharing, and forming equal groups with remainders to do division.

Math Boxes 11✦1

1. Number Sense 6.1 Recognize when an estimate is reasonable in measurements (e.g., closest inch).

2. Number Sense **4.1** Recognize, name, and compare unit fractions from $\frac{1}{12}$ to $\frac{1}{2}$.

3. Number Sense **1.1** Count, read, and write whole numbers to 1,000 and identify the place value for each digit.

4. Number Sense **3.1** Use repeated addition, arrays, and counting by multiples to do multiplication.

5. Number Sense **5.1** Solve problems using combinations of coins and bills.

6. Number Sense **3.0** Students model and solve simple problems involving multiplication and division.

Math Boxes 11✦2

1. Number Sense **2.2** Find the sum or difference of two whole numbers up to three digits long.

2. Statistics, Data Analysis, and Probability 1.3 Identify features of data sets (range and mode).

3. Measurement and Geometry **2.0** Students identify and describe the attributes of common figures in the plane and of common objects in space.

4. Number Sense **3.2** Use repeated subtraction, equal sharing, and forming equal groups with remainders to do division.

5. Statistics, Data Analysis, and Probability 2.1 Recognize, describe, and extend patterns and determine a next term in linear patterns (e.g., 4, 8, 12 . . .; the number of ears on one horse, two horses, three horses, four horses).

6. Statistics, Data Analysis, and Probability 1.3 Identify features of data sets (range and mode).

Math Boxes 11✦3

1. Measurement and Geometry 1.0 Students understand that measurement is accomplished by identifying a unit of measure, iterating (repeating) that unit, and comparing it to the item to be measured.

2. Number Sense **4.1** Recognize, name, and compare unit fractions from $\frac{1}{12}$ to $\frac{1}{2}$.

3. Number Sense **1.1** Count, read, and write whole numbers to 1,000 and identify the place value for each digit.

4. Number Sense **3.1** Use repeated addition, arrays, and counting by multiples to do multiplication.

5. Number Sense **5.1** Solve problems using combinations of coins and bills.

6. Number Sense **3.0** Students model and solve simple problems involving multiplication and division.

Math Boxes 11✦4

1. Number Sense **2.2** Find the sum or difference of two whole numbers up to three digits long.

2. Statistics, Data Analysis, and Probability 1.3 Identify features of data sets (range and mode).

3. Measurement and Geometry **2.0** Students identify and describe the attributes of common figures in the plane and of common objects in space.

4. Number Sense **3.2** Use repeated subtraction, equal sharing, and forming equal groups with remainders to do division.

5. Statistics, Data Analysis, and Probability 2.1 Recognize, describe, and extend patterns and determine a next term in linear patterns (e.g., 4, 8, 12 . . .; the number of ears on one horse, two horses, three horses, four horses).

6. Statistics, Data Analysis, and Probability 1.3 Identify features of data sets (range and mode).

Math Boxes 11✦5

1. Number Sense **3.1** Use repeated addition, arrays, and counting by multiples to do multiplication.

2. Number Sense **3.1** Use repeated addition, arrays, and counting by multiples to do multiplication.

3. Number Sense **2.2** Find the sum or difference of two whole numbers up to three digits long.

4. Statistics, Data Analysis, and Probability 2.2 Solve problems involving simple number patterns.

5. Measurement and Geometry 1.0 Students understand that measurement is accomplished by identifying a unit of measure, iterating (repeating) that unit, and comparing it to the item to be measured.

6. Algebra and Functions 1.3 Solve addition and subtraction problems by using data from simple charts, picture graphs, and number sentences.

Math Boxes 11✦6

1. Number Sense **2.2** Find the sum or difference of two whole numbers up to three digits long.

2. Statistics, Data Analysis, and Probability 1.3 Identify features of data sets (range and mode).

3. Measurement and Geometry **1.3** Measure the length of an object to the nearest inch and/or centimeter.

4. Number Sense **4.2** Recognize fractions of a whole and parts of a group (e.g., one-fourth of a pie, two-thirds of 15 balls).

5. Statistics, Data Analysis, and Probability 2.1 Recognize, describe, and extend patterns and determine a next term in linear patterns (e.g., 4, 8, 12 . . .; the number of ears on one horse, two horses, three horses, four horses).

6. Statistics, Data Analysis, and Probability 1.3 Identify features of data sets (range and mode).

Math Boxes 11•7

1. **Number Sense 3.3** Know the multiplication tables of 2s, 5s, and 10s (to "times 10") and commit them to memory.

2. **Number Sense 3.1** Use repeated addition, arrays, and counting by multiples to do multiplication.

3. **Number Sense 2.2** Find the sum or difference of two whole numbers up to three digits long.

4. **Statistics, Data Analysis, and Probability 2.2** Solve problems involving simple number patterns.

5. **Mathematical Reasoning 1.2** Use tools, such as manipulatives or sketches, to model problems.

6. **Algebra and Functions 1.3** Solve addition and subtraction problems by using data from simple charts, picture graphs, and number sentences.

Math Boxes 11•8

1. **Number Sense 2.2** Find the sum or difference of two whole numbers up to three digits long.

2. **Statistics, Data Analysis, and Probability 1.3** Identify features of data sets (range and mode).

3. **Measurement and Geometry 1.3** Measure the length of an object to the nearest inch and/or centimeter.

4. **Number Sense 4.2** Recognize fractions of a whole and parts of a group (e.g., one-fourth of a pie, two-thirds of 15 balls).

5. **Statistics, Data Analysis, and Probability 2.2** Solve problems involving simple number patterns.

6. **Statistics, Data Analysis, and Probability 1.3** Identify features of data sets (range and mode).

Math Boxes 11•9

1. **Number Sense 3.1** Use repeated addition, arrays, and counting by multiples to do multiplication.

2. **Number Sense 3.3** Know the multiplication tables of 2s, 5s, and 10s (to "times 10") and commit them to memory.

3. **Number Sense 2.2** Find the sum or difference of two whole numbers up to three digits long.

4. **Statistics, Data Analysis, and Probability 2.2** Solve problems involving simple number patterns.

5. **Measurement and Geometry 1.3** Measure the length of an object to the nearest inch and/or centimeter.

6. **Algebra and Functions 1.3** Solve addition and subtraction problems by using data from simple charts, picture graphs, and number sentences.

Math Boxes 11•10

1. **Statistics, Data Analysis, and Probability 1.3** Identify features of data sets (range and mode).

2. **Statistics, Data Analysis, and Probability 1.3** Identify features of data sets (range and mode).

3. **Number Sense 3.0** Students model and solve simple problems involving multiplication and division.

4. **Statistics, Data Analysis, and Probability 1.3** Identify features of data sets (range and mode).

5. **Algebra and Functions 1.3** Solve addition and subtraction problems by using data from simple charts, picture graphs, and number sentences.

6. **Number Sense 3.0** Students model and solve simple problems involving multiplication and division.

Math Boxes 12•1

1. **Number Sense 2.0** Students estimate, calculate, and solve problems involving addition and subtraction of two- and three-digit numbers.

2. **Measurement and Geometry 1.4** Tell time to the nearest quarter hour and know relationships of time (e.g., minutes in an hour, days in a month, weeks in a year).

3. **Number Sense 4.1** Recognize, name, and compare unit fractions from $\frac{1}{12}$ to $\frac{1}{2}$.

4. **Number Sense 5.1** Solve problems using combinations of coins and bills.

5. **Statistics, Data Analysis, and Probability 1.3** Identify features of data sets (range and mode).

6. **Measurement and Geometry 2.1** Describe and classify plane and solid geometric shapes (e.g., circle, triangle, square, rectangle, sphere, pyramid, cube, rectangular prism) according to the number and shape of faces, edges, and vertices.

Math Boxes 12•2

1. **Statistics, Data Analysis, and Probability 1.4** Ask and answer simple questions related to data representations.

2. **Algebra and Functions 1.1** Determine the approach, materials, and strategies to be used.

3. **Number Sense 1.3** Order and compare whole numbers to 1,000 by using the symbols $<$, $=$, $>$.

4. **Measurement and Geometry 2.0** Students identify and describe the attributes of common figures in the plane and of common objects in space.

5. **Measurement and Geometry 1.0** Students understand that measurement is accomplished by identifying a unit of measure, iterating (repeating) that unit, and comparing it to the item to be measured.

6. **Number Sense 4.2** Recognize fractions of a whole and parts of a group (e.g., one-fourth of a pie, two-thirds of 15 balls).

Math Boxes 12•3

1. **Number Sense 2.0** Students estimate, calculate, and solve problems involving addition and subtraction of two- and three-digit numbers.

2. **Number Sense 6.1** Recognize when an estimate is reasonable in measurements (e.g., closest inch).

3. **Number Sense 4.1** Recognize, name, and compare unit fractions from $\frac{1}{12}$ to $\frac{1}{2}$.

4. **Number Sense 5.1** Solve problems using combinations of coins and bills.

5. **Statistics, Data Analysis, and Probability 1.3** Identify features of data sets (range and mode).

6. **Measurement and Geometry 2.1** Describe and classify plane and solid geometric shapes (e.g., circle, triangle, square, rectangle, sphere, pyramid, cube, rectangular prism) according to the number and shape of faces, edges, and vertices.

CA26

Math Boxes 12◆4

1. **Statistics, Data Analysis, and Probability 1.4** Ask and answer simple questions related to data representations.
2. **Algebra and Functions (1.1)** Determine the approach, materials, and strategies to be used.
3. **Number Sense (1.3)** Order and compare whole numbers to 1,000 by using the symbols $<$, $=$, $>$.
4. **Measurement and Geometry (2.0)** Students identify and describe the attributes of common figures in the plane and of common objects in space.
5. **Measurement and Geometry 1.0** Students understand that measurement is accomplished by identifying a unit of measure, iterating (repeating) that unit, and comparing it to the item to be measured.
6. **Number Sense (4.2)** Recognize fractions of a whole and parts of a group (e.g., one-fourth of a pie, two-thirds of 15 balls).

Math Boxes 12◆5

1. **Number Sense 2.3** Use mental arithmetic to find the sum or difference of two two-digit numbers.
2. **Measurement and Geometry 1.4** Tell time to the nearest quarter hour and know relationships of time (e.g., minutes in an hour, days in a month, weeks in a year).
3. **Number Sense (4.1)** Recognize, name, and compare unit fractions from $\frac{1}{12}$ to $\frac{1}{2}$.
4. **Algebra and Functions 1.3** Solve addition and subtraction problems by using data from simple charts, picture graphs, and number sentences.
5. **Measurement and Geometry 1.4** Tell time to the nearest quarter hour and know relationships of time (e.g., minutes in an hour, days in a month, weeks in a year).
6. **Number Sense (2.2)** Find the sum or difference of two whole numbers up to three digits long.

Math Boxes 12◆6

1. **Statistics, Data Analysis, and Probability (1.0)** Students collect numerical data and record, organize, display, and interpret the data on bar graphs and other representations.
2. **Algebra and Functions (1.1)** Determine the approach, materials, and strategies to be used.
3. **Number Sense (1.3)** Order and compare whole numbers to 1,000 by using the symbols $<$, $=$, $>$.
4. **Measurement and Geometry (2.0)** Students identify and describe the attributes of common figures in the plane and of common objects in space.
5. **Measurement and Geometry 1.0** Students understand that measurement is accomplished by identifying a unit of measure, iterating (repeating) that unit, and comparing it to the item to be measured.
6. **Number Sense (4.2)** Recognize fractions of a whole and parts of a group (e.g., one-fourth of a pie, two-thirds of 15 balls).

Math Boxes 12◆7

1. **Number Sense 1.2** Use words, models, and expanded forms (e.g., 45 = 4 tens + 5) to represent numbers (to 1,000).
2. **Number Sense 6.1** Recognize when an estimate is reasonable in measurements (e.g., closest inch).
3. **Number Sense (4.1)** Recognize, name, and compare unit fractions from $\frac{1}{12}$ to $\frac{1}{2}$.
4. **Algebra and Functions 1.3** Solve addition and subtraction problems by using data from simple charts, picture graphs, and number sentences.
5. **Measurement and Geometry 1.4** Tell time to the nearest quarter hour and know relationships of time (e.g., minutes in an hour, days in a month, weeks in a year).
6. **Number Sense (2.2)** Find the sum or difference of two whole numbers up to three digits long.

Math Boxes 12◆8

1. **Number Sense 1.2** Use words, models, and expanded forms (e.g., 45 = 4 tens + 5) to represent numbers (to 1,000).
2. **Measurement and Geometry 1.4** Tell time to the nearest quarter hour and know relationships of time (e.g., minutes in an hour, days in a month, weeks in a year).
3. **Number Sense (4.1)** Recognize, name, and compare unit fractions from $\frac{1}{12}$ to $\frac{1}{2}$.
4. **Algebra and Functions 1.3** Solve addition and subtraction problems by using data from simple charts, picture graphs, and number sentences.
5. **Measurement and Geometry 1.4** Tell time to the nearest quarter hour and know relationships of time (e.g., minutes in an hour, days in a month, weeks in a year).
6. **Number Sense (2.2)** Find the sum or difference of two whole numbers up to three digits long.

LESSON 8·5 Fraction Cards

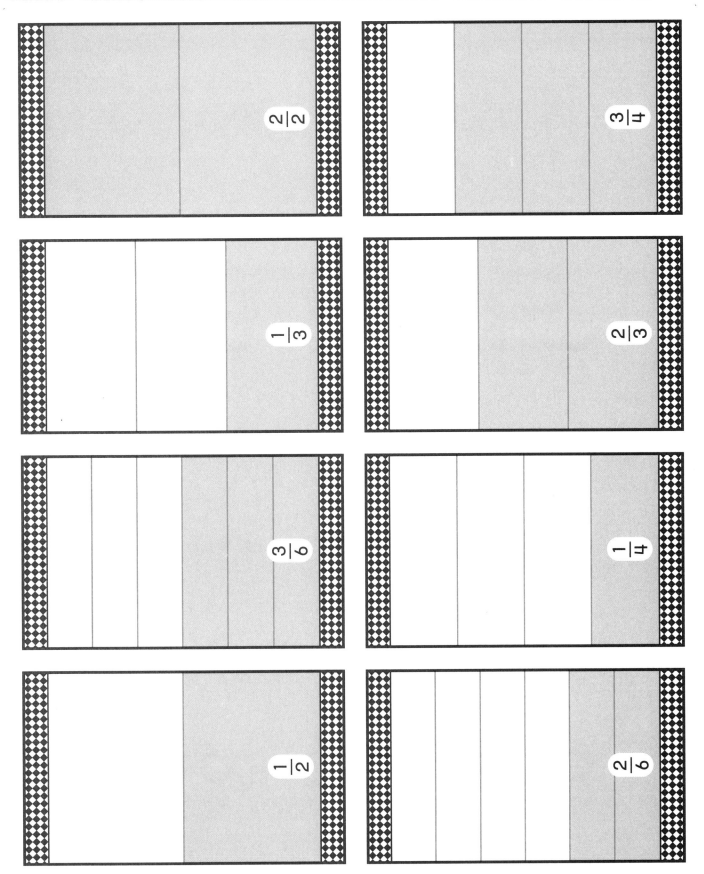

$\dfrac{2}{2}$

$\dfrac{3}{4}$

$\dfrac{1}{3}$

$\dfrac{2}{3}$

$\dfrac{3}{6}$

$\dfrac{1}{4}$

$\dfrac{1}{2}$

$\dfrac{2}{6}$

Activity Sheet 5

LESSON 8·5   **Fraction Cards**

$\dfrac{3}{4}$ $\dfrac{2}{2}$

$\dfrac{2}{3}$ $\dfrac{1}{3}$

$\dfrac{1}{4}$ $\dfrac{3}{6}$

$\dfrac{2}{6}$ $\dfrac{1}{2}$

Back of Activity Sheet 5

LESSON 8·5 Fraction Cards

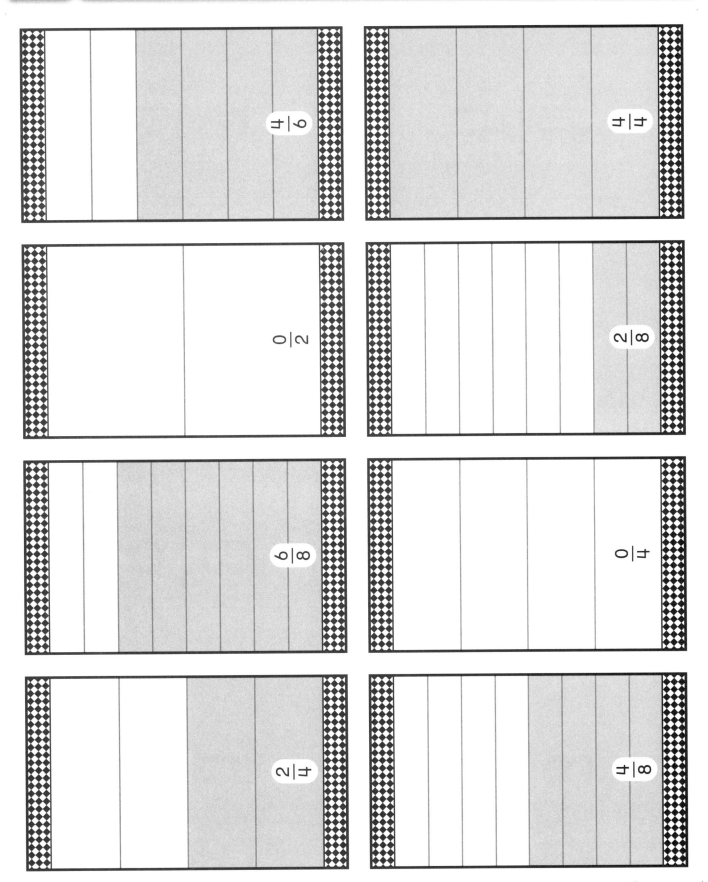

LESSON 8·5   **Fraction Cards**

$$\frac{4}{4} \qquad \frac{4}{6}$$

$$\frac{2}{8} \qquad \frac{0}{2}$$

$$\frac{0}{4} \qquad \frac{6}{8}$$

$$\frac{4}{8} \qquad \frac{2}{4}$$

Back of Activity Sheet 6

LESSON 11·7 ✕, ÷ **Fact Triangles 1**

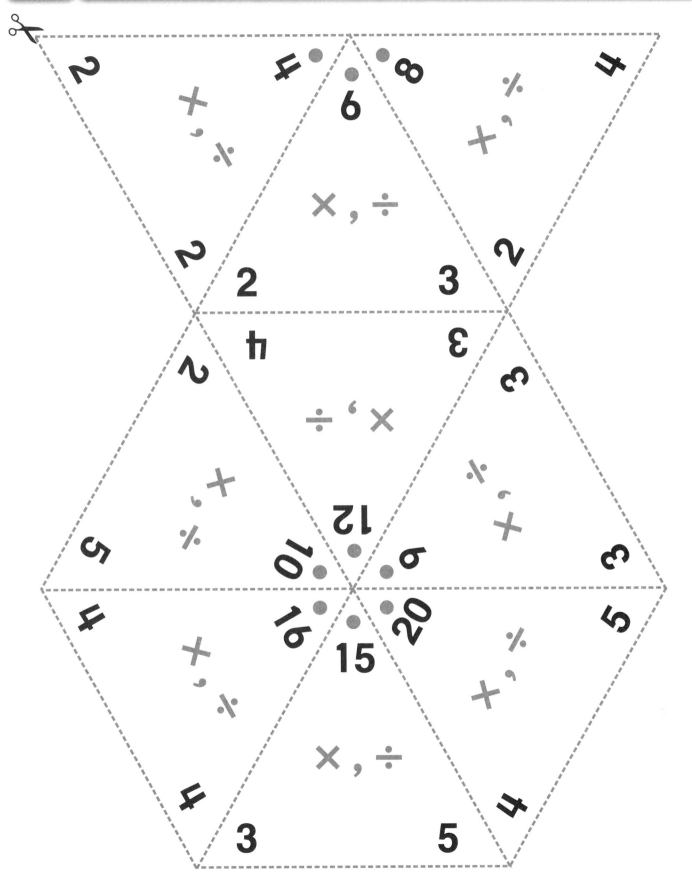

LESSON 11·7 ✕, ÷ **Fact Triangles 2**

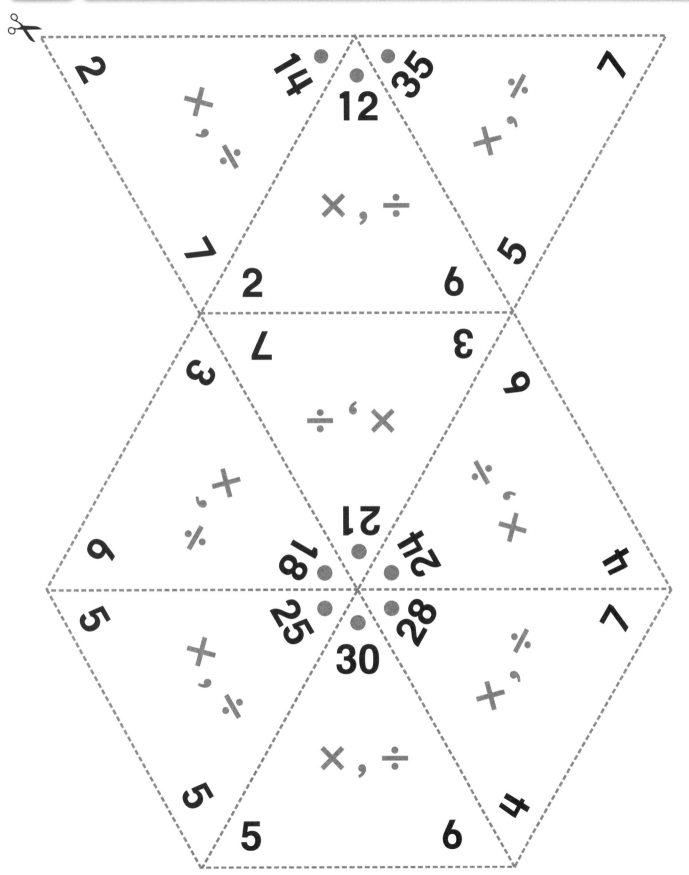

LESSON 11·9   ×, ÷ Fact Triangles 3

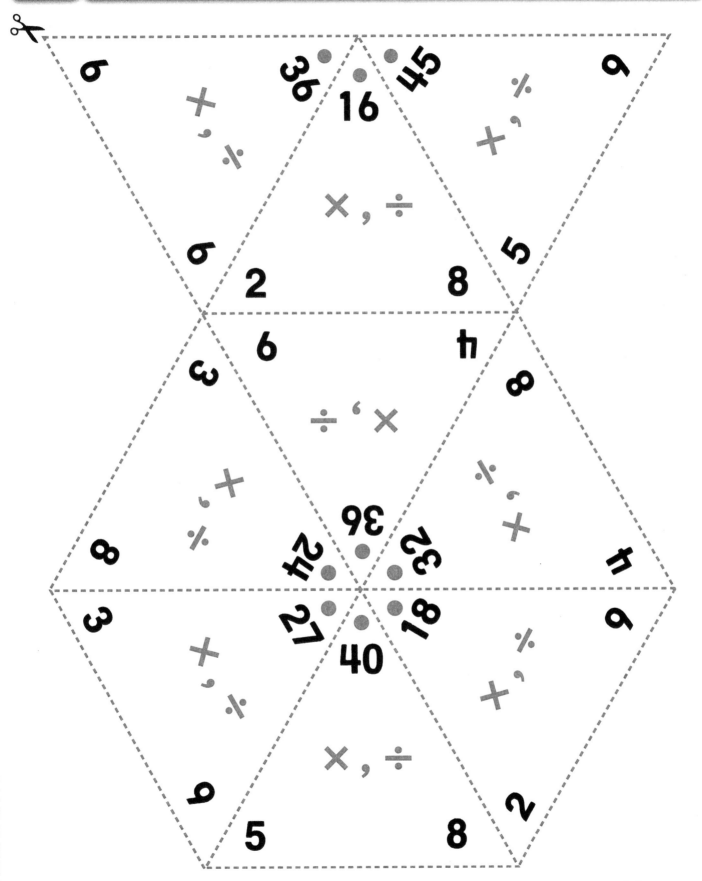

Activity Sheet 9

LESSON 11·9 ×, ÷ Fact Triangles 4

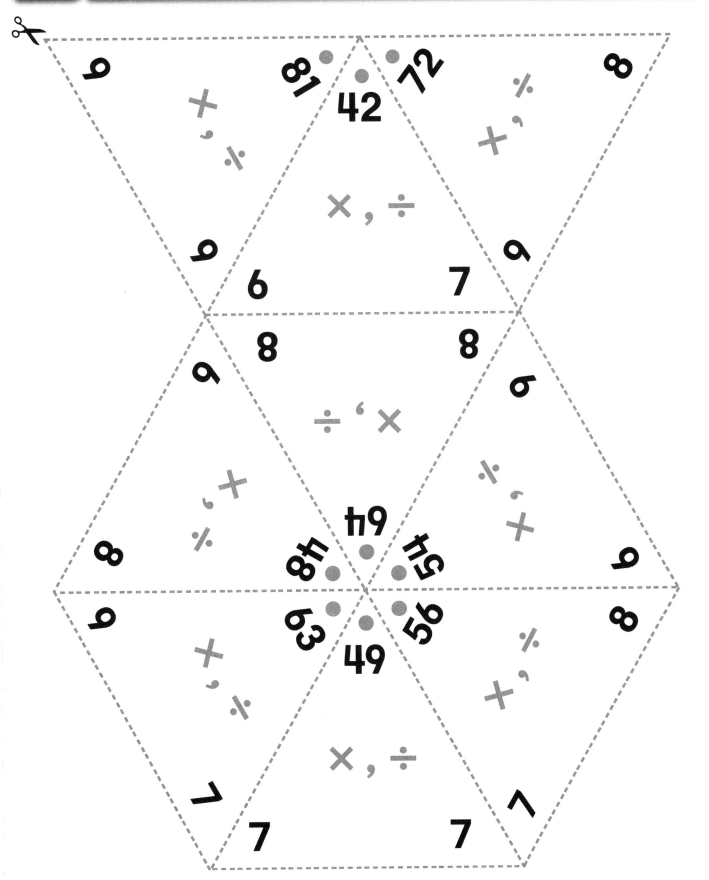